Brabazon

The World's First Jumbo Airliner

Robert Wall

redcliffe

First published in 1999 by Redcliffe Press Ltd.,
81g Pembroke Road, Bristol BS8 3EA

ISBN 1 900178 47 8

British Library Cataloguing in Publication Data
A catalogue record for this book is available from
The British Library

Typeset by Mayhew Typesetting, Rhayader, Powys
and printed by WBC Print, Bridgend, Mid Glamorgan

Contents

Sir George White, 1st Baronet, the Bristol stockbroker and tramway magnate (1854–1916) who founded the Bristol Aeroplane Company.

Introduction

This book has been written to celebrate the first flight of the Bristol Type 167 passenger airliner, the Brabazon Mark I, on Sunday, 4th September, 1949. From design conception to first flight, everything about the Brabazon was big. It was then the largest civil airliner so far conceived and constructed. It required a huge runway, the longest in Europe at the time, for which a rural Gloucestershire village was torn down and flattened. To house this monster aeroplane, the largest set of aircraft hangars anywhere on the planet was built at Filton on the outskirts of Bristol. Both runway and hangar have endured for the remainder of the century, still engaged in the business of producing aeroplanes.

The author joined the Bristol Aeroplane Company's Aircraft Division on 17th September 1947 as an engineering apprentice. This was for a five-year indentured period, and proved to be an exemplary form of education which sadly is no longer available to young people today. After a training period learning to get one's hands dirty and to use basic engineering hand-tools and machines, it was off on a round of the many shops and offices that made up the company in those days.

In theory, one was supposed to stay only six months in each shop, but in November 1949 the author was transferred to the Assembly Hall to join the Brabazon project as a PDA boy supporting draughtsmen on the hangar floor on preliminary drawing alterations – hence PDA! The author was just nineteen years of age and he stayed two and half years with the aeroplane – a never-to-be-forgotten experience which ended with a move to work on the Britannia prototypes. Meanwhile, a part-time course at the Merchant Venturers Technical College in Bristol earned a Higher National Certificate in Mechanical Engineering which allowed him to qualify for a commission in the Technical Branch of the RAF when the time came for National Service.

Many memories remain of those exciting days of the late forties and fifties at Filton but none more poignant than those of the people who made up the company workforce. Many remained from the early days of the firm in 1910–1911, and a huge reservoir of skills abounded. Characters were commonplace but above all there was a loyalty to colleagues and projects which often led to long hours and hard work. It is to the memory of the mentors of those days that this book is affectionately and respectfully dedicated.

Robert Wall, Bristol 1999

ONE

Lift Off!

'I will fly the cockpit and I imagine the rest of
the aeroplane will follow.'

A.J. (Bill) Pegg, Bristol Chief Test Pilot,
Summer 1949

The crowds had come early to the boundaries of Filton airfield that autumn morning in September 1949. The wind was blowing light airs from the east and this was enough to ensure a warm sunny morning. All round the airfield, every vantage spot was crammed with eager Bristolians; some had arrived with the dawn and all were determined not to miss the first flight of the Brab – as the big aeroplane was affectionately known, after the nickname of her conceptor, the aviation pioneer Lord Brabazon of Tara. He it was who in 1942 had set up a Cabinet Committee to report on the types of civil airliner that Great Britain would need after the war had been fought to a successful conclusion. In all, his committee had recommended five types of machine and the first, the Brabazon I was about to fly – seven years later. This day would see the veteran aviator's latest triumph, coming from the same man who, in 1909, took off with a piglet in a basket strapped alongside him to prove that pigs might fly!

Ground running of the Brabazon's coupled Centaurus piston engines (jets were still in their infancy) had been completed earlier in the week and Saturday had been used to carry out a number of ground runs. This had been done to test the big aeroplane's handling qualities and that September Saturday a total of ten runs in all had been completed. The last run proved by far the most exciting. Test pilot Pegg and his nine-man crew had been steadily working up to the 75-knot deadline at which take off was forecast. Pegg was handling a Bristol prototype for the first time and he was meticulous in his preparation. Earlier in 1949, he had spent some time in the USA, flying the giant Convair B36 bomber to gain experience of large machines. Pegg put this experience to good use when, on the tenth run, the nose lifted smack on 75 knots and the Brab was almost airborne before being persuaded back onto the runway. Runs over, she was towed away to the hangar for an all-night inspection. The only major snag was with the nose wheel steering which was disconnected for the first flight.

'ALL WELL AND READY' trumpeted the Bristol *Evening World's* last edition, confidently predicting a flight on the morrow, as the crowds dispersed.

They were back the next morning, Sunday 4th September, in even greater numbers. A good view of the hangar and runway could be had from the Filton golf course and hundreds gathered there. Another huge crowd was on the A38 Gloucester–Bristol trunk road at the east end of the runway, where the Runway Garage still remained in a somewhat exposed position. The crowds had quite a wait while the aircraft was readied.

In fact, Bill Pegg and his little band of aircrew were on the verge of becoming national heroes. Television was still in its infancy and the boost it would get from the coronation was four years away. But this was the heyday of the cinema, and to Filton flocked the world's newsreel cameramen and their kit, all struggling for better vantage points along the runway.

Meanwhile, armies of VIP guests and anyone else with the slightest excuse to be present were arriving at the site, where they would be entertained by the Bristol board under the leadership of the son of the company's founder, Sir G. Stanley White, Bart. There was a minor hiatus when Lord Brabazon's pass was found to be out of order and a works security officer almost refused him entry. In the interim, the normal business of the factory and airfield continued. The helicopter rotor buzzed away and on the north side of the field, a row of Vampire F1 fighters of 501 (County of Gloucester) Squadron RAAF were being prepared for later sorties. 501 Squadron had something like legendary status to Bristolians. This all arose from events in 1940. Until the spring of that epic year, 501 Squadron Hurricanes had kept a watchful eye on the city and its day-to-day affairs. Then they were switched to the thick of the air battles over France and later over Britain. 'Just you wait!' said knowing Bristol folk. Sure enough, at mid-day on 25th September 1940, an unimpeded force of Heinkel 111s emptied 168 bombs onto The Bristol Aeroplane works, killing 91 personnel in bombed air raid shelters. The physical damage was not as bad as it appeared and next day a Polish fighter squadron landed at Filton. Now, nine years later, their successors were lined up to greet the new giant. Later that day, so a 501 veteran relates, the squadron flew their Vampires from the Filton airfield in tribute to the Brabazon.

The Bristol Type 167 Brabazon I in flight, 13th October, 1949.

Expectation soared when, about 1045hrs, the Brabazon was towed from the hangar to the east end of the main runway and engine warming was started. Light loading of 210,000lb (including 4,000 gallons of fuel) was the order of the day.

Bill Pegg had succeeded the legendary Captain Cyril Uwins as Bristol chief test pilot, after Uwins had flown his 'last' first flight in the Type 170 Freighter. Since then Pegg had spent much time rehearsing the Brabazon's first flight and with him on board that day he had as aircrew: co-pilot Walter Gibb DSO, DFC., chief flight observer M.J. Peniston, chief flight engineer L.D. Atkinson, flight engineer H.J. Hayman, flight engineer A. Cowan, flight test observer Malcolm West, flight test observer John Sizer, flight test observer John Cochrane, electrical engineer Ken Fitzgerald.

At last the Brab began to move westward and vanished over the famous hump in the runway to the west end of the strip where Pegg turned her into the wind, which was already veering into a cross-wind of eight knots or so. Then he eased the throttles forward and the great machine, rumbling down the runway with a dignified roar, rose in the air after little more than 500 yards.

As she did so, she appeared to hesitate momentarily, then continue her stately ascent. This was in response to test co-pilot Walter Gibb adjusting the throttles to lower the nose which Pegg had allowed to get too high. Many years later, in a BBC interview, Walter was to comment wryly, 'that's what co-pilots are for!' The flight proceeded for 27 minutes until Pegg landed safely after a northern circuit of the airfield without raising the undercarriage.

Despite the doubts of many, and two years late, the Brabazon had flown. Many who watched that day were survivors of the Bristol blitz who had lost husbands and relatives in World War II. Shortages of consumer goods persisted and food rationing was still in place. Life in Britain was drab and comfortless. So the great silver aeroplane in the Gloucestershire sky represented hope for the future and prosperity to come. No wonder spontaneous cheers broke out all around the airfield, while a party of RAF officers threw their hats in the air. Congratulations were the order of the day and as soon as the big aircraft had taxied to a standstill with its sixteen propellers stationary, the crew climbed out to the cheers of all. Telegrams poured in from around the country and the world.

The Minister for Civil Aviation, Lord Pakenham (later the Earl of Longford), said, 'Heartiest congratulations to you and all the company's workforce on your magnificent achievement.' His fellow minister, for Supply, George Strauss,

The flight test crew on the first flight, Sunday, 4th September, 1949: (l. to r.) A. Cowan (flight test observer), M.W. West (flight engineer), M.J. Peniston (chief flight test observer), W. Gibb (co-pilot), A.J. Pegg (pilot), J. Sizer (flight test observer), H.J. Hayman (flight engineer), L.D. Atkinson (chief flight engineer), K.A. Fitzgerald (electrical engineer), J.M. Cochrane (flight test observer).

A.J. 'Bill' Pegg, the Bristol chief test pilot who handled the first flight of the Brabazon on Sunday, September 4th, 1949.

12

Walter F. Gibb, DSO, DFC, who was co-pilot on the first flight, and later succeeded Pegg as chief test pilot. He did most of the Brabazon development flying and was a holder of the world altitude record.

13

whose ministry was paying for it all, forecast that 'this first flight foreshadows the time when Britain's civil aircraft will lead the world'. There was much more in the same vein. Even Lord Brabazon was heard to say 'My faith has been vindicated'.

But had it? Few people with doubts could be found at Filton that lovely September morning of 1949 and none was willing to voice them. There must have been a handful around who remembered that far off day in 1909 when old 'Brab' had taken his pig aloft to prove that pigs might fly. Had something of the same occurred forty years on? Only time would tell.

TWO

Genesis – Born in the thirties

'All aircraft are designed and built in the light
of past experience.'

*Dr. A.E. Russell, Chief Engineer,
Bristol Aeroplane Co, 1951*

The Bristol Aeroplane Company was founded on 19th February, 1910 by the Bristol tramway millionaire, Sir George White, who already possessed a large fortune from his public transport activities and a prosperous stockbroking partnership. Sir George was no aviator – indeed there is no record of his ever having flown – but he was unique in early British aviation for a very good reason. Unlike his contemporaries such as Roe, Handley Page and De Havilland, George White entered the aeroplane business for the sole purpose of making money.

George White began producing his Boxkite aircraft in the tramway shed at Filton and had the first one in the air by 30th July 1910. Realising that aircraft needed pilots, Sir George set up the famous Bristol flying schools soon after, and they became a steady source of income, particularly when aircraft sales were low. The Bristol flying schools at Larkhill and later at Filton became well established on the British aviation scene and lasted until the nineteen fifties.

In the early years, George White called his company by the alternative name of The British and Colonial Aeroplane Company. The name Bristol did not come into full use until after World War I in 1919. From the beginning, it was in every sense a 'family' business where all controlling positions were occupied by Sir George or members of his family, which included a host of nephews and cousins with the soubriquet of Smith. All the original funds for the Bristol company came from private family sources, while White's chairmanship of the Western Wagon and Property Company allowed him to borrow the remaining capital he required. Onto the Bristol board he brought his brother Samuel and his son

15

Stanley, while his nephew Henry White Smith became secretary and his cousin Sidney Smith, general manager. With Sidney came another cousin, Herbert Thomas, who would later also become general manager at Filton. The company was already in those early days being referred to by Bristolians as BAC, a habit which the citizens have never lost through numerous name changes over the century. Very early on, there were cynics who claimed that BAC stood for 'Brothers and Cousins'.

In due course, this family dominance of the company was to have important consequences for the history of Bristol aviation and even impacted on the Brabazon. However, in 1910, there were few who denied George White the right to do what he liked with his own money and many who considered that he was pouring it down the drain in his aviation venture.

Until World War I broke out in August 1914, commercial success on any significant scale eluded the Bristol company. By that time, however, it had recruited a skilled workforce mostly from its own tramway workers and tried and rejected a series of different designers and their schemes. The one designer that Bristol retained from that era was a Scottish marine engineer called Frank Barnwell who by 1914 had produced the Bristol Scout, the world's first fighter aircraft. The war meant large commercial contracts for Bristol even if it also meant working to other designs (for example, the RAE's BE2), and additional accommodation was built at Filton.

Then, in 1916, Barnwell and his talented assistant, Leslie Frise, produced a world beating twin-seat scout, The Bristol F2B Fighter, which triumphed over the Imperial German airforce on the Western Front and went on to a production run of over 5,000 copies. The Fighter founded the fortunes of the Bristol Aeroplane Company, but in one of life's tragic ironies, Sir George did not live to enjoy his triumph, dying of a heart attack on 22nd November, 1916. He was succeeded by his son, Stanley.

If the family nature of the Bristol business was the first feature to impact on the Brabazon story, then the recruitment in 1920 of Roy Fedden, along with the Cosmos Engineering Company and its Jupiter engine, was surely the second. Fedden, his design team and the total equipment of Cosmos, together with several RAF contracts, was knocked down to Bristol for £15,000, one of the commercial bargains of the century.

Roy Fedden is one of aviation's all-time greats. He dominated the British aero-engine business for almost three decades; and his series of successful air-cooled radial engines, which culminated in the huge sleeve-valve Hercules and

The Brabazon Mk I, registered G-AGPW, taking off for its first flight from Filton on Sunday, 4th September, 1949.

Leslie Frise, chief engineer of the Bristol Aeroplane Company from 1938 to 1946. He succeeded Frank Barnwell on the latter's death in an aircraft accident and, with Archibald Russell, was one of the leaders in the design of the Brabazon.

18

Centaurus, did much to assist the winning of the air conflict in World War II. His first engine, the 500hp Jupiter, was, after a hesitant start, adopted by the RAF and a large number of civilian operators, to become by far the most successful aero-engine of the nineteen twenties.

This was just as well, for the same decade saw many aircraft prototypes fly at Filton without securing any subsequent production orders. Only the Bulldog fighter which Barnwell and Frise produced at the end of the decade sold in any numbers – over 500 – and the income from the Jupiter proved vital to company success.

Roy Fedden was a Bristolian from Stoke Bishop who claimed his family was distinguished in Bristol for many generations before the Whites appeared. He was educated at Clifton and went into engineering straight from school. There is no doubt that Fedden was a natural engineering genius, but he also possessed a ruthless ambition. It says much for Fedden that throughout his career at Bristol he was surrounded by a devoted band of engineers who supported him in good times and bad. On the other hand, despite his successes, the Bristol directors would not appoint Fedden to the main board. He was not 'one of them' and would always remain an employee. This set up resentments that would eventually lead to industrial and commercial mistakes. In the meantime, most of Fedden's staff worked all week plus two night shifts and Saturday morning. One day, his assistant Frank Owner asked, 'Are you ever satisfied?' Came the great man's reply 'Certainly not! That would be a terrible state to be in!'

So, as the nineteen thirties dawned, the Bristol Aeroplane Company was a well established manufacturer of aircraft and aero-engines, with Bulldog fighters in production at Filton and the well tried Jupiter on the line at Patchway, the new plant which had been built as a result of Fedden's industry.

Nevertheless these were difficult years for the Bristol company. When Bulldog production ended in 1934, the Filton plant was virtually at a standstill and only the winning of a contract to build 141 copies of the Hawker Audax day bomber kept the workforce intact. A steady flow of Fedden's Jupiter and Pegasus engines from Patchway in the meantime ensured the firm's commercial health. This was just as well for events in places far from Bristol were about to give the infant aircraft business a considerable boost worldwide. They would also set the scene which would eventually lead to the production of the Brabazon airliner.

These events were two-fold and occurred four thousand miles apart. The first was the re-organisation in 1930 of the US mail's postal services. The other was the coming to power of Adolf Hitler in Germany on 30th January, 1933 and the consequent rise of Fascism, bringing with it the spectre of total war in Europe. These seemingly unconnected events were to have huge consequences for the aircraft industry on both sides of the Atlantic. In Europe, aircraft development was almost exclusively concentrated on military machines as each side re-armed at break-neck speed.

In the United States the decade had begun with a drastic reorganisation of air services carried out by Walter Brown, Postmaster-General under President Herbert Hoover. Brown saw clearly that the existing chaos of small airlines in the United States could not continue, and he set about forcing mergers with a ruthlessness that had seldom been seen in US government policy. Small operators were forced out of business as the United States Post Office awarded the bulk of the airmail to a relative handful of airlines which were considered to be well run and financially sound.

In May 1930, Brown invited to Washington the heads of the large airlines for a meeting which later became known as the Spoils Conference. It was an appropriate name as the spoils were divided between those lines that went along with Brown's plans to set up three main mail routes across the breadth of America. United Airways were given the northern route, the newly formed American Airlines got the southern and the central went to Transcontinental and Western Air Express, later to become the legendary TWA.

Brown's scheme prospered until 1934 when he was caught up in a financial scandal which led to his being convicted of malpractice. The new President Franklin Roosevelt resolved to reform the postal scheme but only with airlines that had no links with aircraft manufacturers. So Boeing had to break its long standing tie-up with United, and other aircraft builders gave up their interests in TWA, Eastern and American Airways. This decision to end the link between airline and manufacturer gave America a free market at a crucial time when the demand for air transport in the US was soaring as the nation recovered from economic depression.

The demand for new aircraft meant that the emphasis in the States was largely on the production of fast, economic and safe civil airliners and led directly to the creation of the great Douglas DC3, the most successful machine ever to enter production. It came about in this way. The depression forced the motor industry to retrench by withdrawal from the aircraft business. This left Boeing, Douglas and Lockheed as fully independent operators and they dominated world air transport development thereafter, until the European Airbus challenge of the nineteen nineties.

The ubiquitous Douglas DC3, workhorse of the world's airlines at the time the Brabazon was produced, and the most successful civil aircraft ever. (courtesy: Janes).

Having won the coast-to-coast mail contract, United went to Boeing for an aircraft capable of operating over that distance. The result was the all-metal Boeing 247, introduced in March 1933, and able to fly coast-to-coast in 20 hours. The 247 was years ahead of anything possessed by the Europeans and is rightly regarded as the first modern airliner and the forerunner of a whole series of successful Boeing machines. United ordered 60, which tied up the assembly lines at Seattle for well over a year. TWA and American Airlines had to look elsewhere. They settled on Douglas Aircraft Inc., of Santa Monica, California.

In 1932 Jack Frye, the boss of TWA, had gone to Donald Douglas for a tri-motor airplane. At the time Douglas was working on something he considered much better. The result was the DC1 which could carry more passengers than the Boeing and rapidly developed into the DC2. Douglas' gamble paid off when TWA ordered 20 DC2s. Eventually he went on to build 220 DC2s, while developing the DC3. So successful was the Douglas series of airliners that only 75 of the Boeing 247 were built.

The Douglas DC3 first flew on 17th December, 1935 and in all about 11,000 copies were eventually built. The type first saw service on American Airlines New York–Chicago service in June, 1936. It was an all-metal, low-wing monoplane with a wingspan of 96ft (29m) and the range extended to 1300 miles (2092km). It was bought by every prominent airline worldwide and was the main transport aircraft of the Allied airforces in World War II. Most importantly, it established the American industry as the leading force in airliner production, which would have serious implications for British projects, such as the Brabazon, in future years.

While these exciting events were unfolding in America, the British industry continued to expend its major efforts on military projects directly linked to re-armament against the threat posed by Germany. Such civil airliner projects as existed were very small orders placed by the national flag carrier, Imperial Airways. The main suppliers were Handley Page, Armstrong Whitworth and De Havilland.

Imperial Airways entered the thirties with an order to Handley Page for eight of the giant HP42 bi-planes, driven by four of Fedden's ever present Jupiter engines. These gangling machines with their Warren girder pattern struts came to be the trade mark of Imperial Airways as they made their way from London Croydon to Paris Le Bourget at 90mph maximum, and far less in a headwind. These HP42s served right up to the outbreak of war in 1939 and were joined by more modern aircraft such as the Armstrong Whitworth Ensign and the De

Havilland Frobisher. The quantities were always small, however, and at no time did the British industry come anywhere near to producing an aircraft that could rival the DC3. Even the newly formed British Airways in 1938 bought American Lockheed Super Electras for its European services, and Prime Minister Neville Chamberlain flew in one of these to meet Hitler in Munich in September of that year.

Britain did, nevertheless, produce one classic aeroplane in the thirties that has gone into the history books, and which had a profound influence on the later design of the Brabazon. This was the Short S.23 Empire Class flying boat which was designed to alight on river, lake or ocean, carrying large payloads of passengers, freight and mails.

When, in 1935, the British Government announced the Empire Air Mail scheme which provided for air carriage of all mails on Empire routes, the current equipment available to Imperial Airways was incapable of operating the new schedules.

A new aircraft was required and a contract was placed with Short Bros. of Rochester, the British flying boat experts, for an initial batch of 28 machines ordered straight off the drawing board, an unheard of practice in those days. 24 passengers were to be carried and up to a ton of mail. A cruising speed of 155mph was required and this was obtained by using four of Fedden's latest Pegasus radial engines, each delivering 950hp. The Pegasus was one of the best engines ever to come out of Patchway and fully vindicated its choice for the S.23.

The services operated by the S.23 opened in February 1937 and soon the great boats were a familiar sight, starting from their base at Hythe on Southampton Water and flying as far as Australia, operating through Egypt, India and Malaya via Singapore, Darwin to Brisbane.

The highest standards for passengers were offered by the Empire boats and many travel experts claim that these have never been surpassed. The cabins were roomy, with large, spacious armchairs, and there was a promenade area especially provided with windows that gave a clear view of the scenery passing below. A separate smoking room was available and the food, mostly cooked on board, consisted of such items as fricasée of chicken, roast fillet of veal, poached salmon écosse and even crêpe suzettes prepared at the table. In an age which expected this kind of service in its ocean liners – like the *Queen Elizabeth* and the *Queen Mary* – the airlines had high standards to meet.

In the event, the standards provided on the Empire flying boats were to prove the undoing of the Brabazon project. The big machine was designed to be not

The Short S.23 Empire Class flying boat of Imperial Airways which largely inspired the passenger standards specified for the Brabazon. (courtesy: BA).

that much faster than the flying boat and the luxury accommodation provided was certainly modelled on that of the Short aeroplane. A glossy prospectus put out when Brabazon was in production showed a double-decker arrangement, with first-class private bedrooms, lounge, cocktail bar and 32-seater cinema. Given Brabazon's ponderous speed – she was planned to cruise at 250 miles an hour – perhaps this degree of luxury would have been needed to make the long-haul flight from London to New York bearable.

The prospectus went on in up-beat fashion to suggest that 'with three aircraft allotted to the route – two operating and one in reserve – seven services a week in each direction could be maintained. The degree of comfort provided by Brabazon merits special attention. It would be possible to leave London after a full evening's engagement, sleep through the crossing, and arrive in New York early the next morning, refreshed and ready for any business engagements. A day later, a passenger could be back in London . . . A service giving speed with utmost comfort, an essential unit in the network of North Atlantic airlines.'

All this led inevitably to an airliner that was too slow for its intended route, with standards that were too costly to operate profitably. At the end of the thirties – ten years before Brabazon's maiden flight – the Americans had already glimpsed the promise of a mass market for aviation, while in Britain flying was still considered the luxurious privilege of the wealthy few.

Meanwhile, at Bristol, the Filton and Patchway factories were now engaged in the re-armament race and the productive capacity of both factories was being expanded rapidly. At Filton, production lines were being laid down for the Bristol Type 142M Blenheim light bomber for which an order of 150 was obtained in September 1935. From 4,200 in June of that year the Filton payroll leapt to 8,233 by Christmas. The Blenheim had originated from a light transport called the Britain First which had been designed by Barnwell for the newspaper magnate Lord Rothermere. It was powered by two of Fedden's latest engine, the Mercury, and on trials proved to be faster than any current RAF fighter aircraft. A light bomber version was quickly developed and production started. By the time war broke out in 1939, the Blenheim was available to the RAF in quantity and was its most numerous aircraft on active service. Although by now obsolescent, it sustained the service in the first year of the war, and did valiant work throughout the war in the Mediterranean. In all, 6,212 Blenheims of all versions were built, and with it the lean years of the Aircraft Division were over and the factory expanded into one of the largest aircraft plants in Europe. Despite the tragic death of Captain Frank Barnwell in a light aircraft crash on 2nd August,

1938, the design team he had built up was now capable of producing a wide variety of projects. Barnwell was succeeded by Leslie Frise who set work in progress on a torpedo bomber, a twin-engined fighter and a Blenheim replacement which would later become the Beaufort, Beaufighter and Brigand. Also prominent at Filton on the engineering staff was A.E. Russell (later Dr. Sir Archibald Russell) who was a structures expert. Russell was already giving his attention to the problems facing the design-and-build of large airframes.

At Patchway, Fedden's reign continued and here the expansion schemes were even greater as the staff struggled to increase output of the Pegasus and Mercury, and the much improved Perseus, Taurus and Hercules engines which had the new sleeve valve gear, delivering much increased power. Such was the demand for these engines that Fedden and the Air Ministry set up a scheme to create shadow factories based on the motor industry. Six in all were built, one at Patchway becoming the famous No 2 Shadow, and five more in the Midlands.

At this time Fedden began to plan what was to be his greatest engine, the 2000hp Centaurus. This was the engine that would eventually power the Brabazon I and it confirmed Fedden as the leader in piston engine design. His success with this engine and the earlier Hercules vindicated his faith in the large air-cooled radial engine. This faith was to be well justified as far as it went, but in the end would prove a liability to the Bristol company for one particular reason: the invention in both Britain and Germany of the gas turbine aircraft engine.

As the world now knows, the father of the jet engine was Air Commodore Sir Frank Whittle, a British engineer who began work for his company, Power Jets, in the early thirties. By 1941, he had an engine in the air, proof of the viability of the project and already attracting the attention of the aero-engine industry.

Lord Hives and Stanley Hooker of Rolls-Royce, Sir Frank Spriggs of Armstrong-Siddeley and Geoffrey de Havilland all wanted to design and build the new engines, which they rightly considered were the power units of the future. De Havilland even had an engine running by 1942 and Rolls were not far behind.

At Bristol, the position was different, largely because of Fedden's commitment to the piston engine and his view that gas turbines were an unnecessary diversion from the main war effort, which was to produce piston engines in more powerful versions and ever greater numbers. This was contrary to the view of Filton's rising star, Reginald Verdon Smith, a member of the White family, holder of a first in law from Oxford and director in charge of the shadow factories. A friend of Stanley Hooker from university days, Verdon Smith was well aware of Rolls'

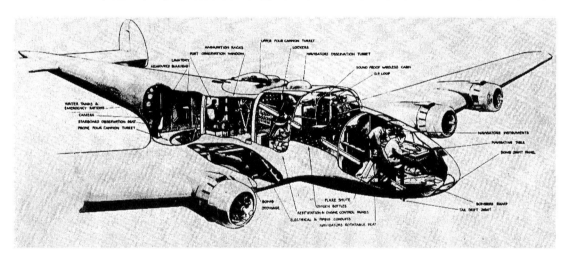

An artist's impression of the Bristol Type 159, a proposed heavy bomber of 1939, with four Hercules engines, 114ft span and 300 mph. It never flew but gave Frise experience of large aircraft design.

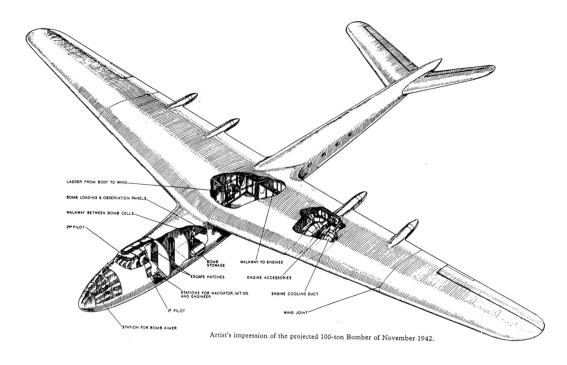

LADDER FROM BODY TO WING
BOMB LOADING & OBSERVATION PANELS
WALKWAY BETWEEN BOMB CELLS
2ⁿᵈ PILOT
BOMB STOWAGE
WALKWAY TO ENGINES
ESCAPE HATCHES
ENGINE ACCESSORIES
STATIONS FOR NAVIGATOR, W/T OR. AND ENGINEER
ENGINE COOLING DUCT
1ˢᵗ PILOT
WING JOINT
STATION FOR BOMB AIMER

Artist's impression of the projected 100-ton Bomber of November 1942.

The proposed 100-ton bomber of 1942, which was turned down by the RAF who preferred to rely on the well tried Lancasters and Halifaxs. Unusually it was not allotted a Bristol type number but its design was developed into that of the Brabazon.

The Convair B36 inter-continental bomber was the world's largest aircraft in series production at the time of the Brabazon's first flight. They had the same wing span of 230ft. Chief test pilot Bill Pegg visited the US to fly the B46 to gain experience of large aircraft handling. (courtesy: USAF).

progress on jets and wished Bristol to be in the same position. Eventually, in February 1941, Fedden set up a study group under Frank Owner for the design of a big gas turbo-prop but he later halved the proposed power. At this point, Bristol began to fall behind in jet development although this study led eventually to the Bristol Theseus turbo-prop (which was not a success) and on to the Proteus, a turbo-prop which was proposed for the Brabazon II in a coupled version. This engine was not ready in time for the Brabazon but did fly in the giant Saunders-Roe Princess flying boat. The Proteus would eventually be redesigned by Stanley Hooker and fly successfully in all the production models of the Bristol Britannia.

By this time, relations between Fedden and the Bristol board were at a low ebb. The cause of the problem was what the board saw as Fedden's mismanagement of the engine production line which led to ever increasing costs. Fedden still resented the fact that he had not been appointed to the board. Eventually on 1st October, 1942, Fedden was dismissed and asked to leave the firm's premises. Fedden had many friends in high places (including Lord Brabazon who raised the matter in the House of Lords), who saw to it that he was taken on as a Government consultant.

Two of the essentials for the Brabazon design, the passenger requirements and the power plants, were now in place although no one realised it at the time. The third element, the airframe, was also to emerge eventually from design studies prepared at Filton in the form of two heavy bombers, neither of which in fact ever flew.

In October 1938, Leslie Frise submitted a design for the Bristol Type 159, a four-engined heavy bomber with Hercules engines, 114ft wingspan, capable of 300mph and a range of 3,500 miles. The design was eventually dropped because of the heavy demand for fighter aircraft in 1940, but experience with wind tunnel models and mock-up gave Frise and Russell the confidence that they were capable of building such a large aircraft.

Then, little over a year later, when the danger posed by the Luftwaffe had receded and the RAF had gone over to the offensive, Bristol was asked to prepare designs for a much larger bomber with a payload of 80,000lbs, more than the total weight of the Type 159. The result of this work never received a Bristol type number and was known among the staff at Filton as the 'Hundred Ton Bomber'. By the time the final design studies were ready in November 1942, the bomber was a giant machine of 225ft span, 225,000lb all-up weight, powered by eight Centaurus engines coupled in pairs and buried in the wings

The largest Bristol-built aeroplane prior to the Brabazon, the Type 130 Bombay troop carrier which first flew on 23rd June, 1935 in the hands of Captain Uwins. The cantilever wing spanned 95ft 9in and 50 were built by Shorts in Belfast, giving robust service in World War II.

with pusher airscrews. With a large butterfly tail, it was by any standards an elegant machine but the design was rejected in favour of increased production of Lancasters, the well proved type in service with Bomber Command.

The Hundred Ton Bomber was the third element of the Brabazon's conception and now, just before Christmas 1942, events conspired which led directly to its genesis.

THREE

Enter Lord Brabazon

'This type . . . should at once capture for
the country the Blue Riband of the air.'

Brabazon Committee Report, October 1945

The war years from 1939 to 1945 saw the United Kingdom come closer to
corporate dictatorship than at any time since Cromwell's Commonwealth. The
Emergency Powers Acts gave Churchill's coalition government complete powers
over all citizens, albeit with the consent of the mass of the population. The
government determined what and how much people ate, what sorts of clothes they
wore, where they worked, where they were allowed to travel and, in some cases,
even where they lived. Whole communities from coastal areas were moved inland
and private houses requisitioned by the thousand for the use of the military, while
good farmland became airfields almost over night. All this was accepted for the
sake of the 'war effort' by an ungrudging populace determined to defeat the Nazis.

Hence, it came as no surprise to anyone when towards the end of 1942, the
Government announced that it was giving attention to the types of civil aircraft
that Britain would need in the years of peace that would follow an Allied victory.
That victory now looked more assured, and, just as Government action had seen
fighter and bomber aircraft provided by the Ministry of Aircraft Production under
Lord Beaverbrook, now that same example would be applied to civil equipment.
Furthermore, a ministry delegation had visited America in 1942 and returned with
a clear impression of the lead that country enjoyed in research and development of
civil machines, not to mention the huge production facilities available. Britain
would be hard pushed to keep up if action was not taken now.

At the same time, there originated in the UK a story that the two governments
had agreed in 1941 that Britain would concentrate her aircraft production on
military machines, leaving the US to produce the transport aircraft required by

the alliance. While this story has never been corroborated, it is a fact that by mid-war, when the US was producing the DC3, C46, Constellation, DC4 and Stratocruiser in large numbers, the British industry could offer only small batches of converted bomber designs such as the Avro Lancastrian and York, and the HP Halton.

To initiate their policy, the Government created an inter-departmental committee which was placed under the chairmanship of Lord Brabazon of Tara, a newly created peer who was Chairman of the Air Registration Board. J.T.C. Moore-Brabazon was one of the founding fathers of British aviation. He was born in 1884 at Tara in County Meath and attended Harrow and Cambridge, where he became a close friend of Charles Rolls. He became the first Briton to fly an aeroplane (a Voisin) in the United Kingdom. This was in April, 1909, just beating A.V. Roe, and 'Brab', as he was always known, became the holder of British pilot's licence No.1. During these pioneer years, he engaged in ballooning, motor and motorcycle racing, and raced bobsleighs down the Cresta run, something he continued until well into his seventies.

Following the death of Charles Rolls in an aircraft accident at Bournemouth in July 1910, Brabazon's wife persuaded him to give up flying. However, he became a leading advocate of the science, and later, when he entered parliament as a Conservative MP, he was always vocal in support of aviation development.

By 1942, Brabazon was serving in Churchill's cabinet as Minister of Aircraft Production, having succeeded the great Lord Beaverbrook who was Lord Privy Seal. Brab, never one to guard his tongue, voiced some pertinent but incautious thoughts about Britain's Russian allies at a private dinner party which were immediately leaked to the press. Churchill was reluctantly forced to seek his resignation, but he left with a peerage and was immediately available to take the chair of the Brabazon Committee to review and make recommendations for the future of civil aviation.

Brabazon set up his committee in the penultimate week of 1942 with headquarters at 70 Pall Mall, London. He had a staff of four, and the committee was made up of senior officials of the Ministry of Aircraft Production, with the Director of Civil Aviation William Hildred. Alan Campbell Orde of BOAC represented the airlines but in effect put the interests of BOAC first every time. In addition, he was an enthusiast for American equipment, placing the order for the Super Electras which BA had bought in 1938. The industry was represented by Geoffrey de Havilland, whose abomination of committees was well known in the business, although he was later to admit that this one was 'not so bad'. Also

33

lurking in the wings was the ever enduring figure of Sir Wilfred Freeman, Permanent Secretary at the Air Ministry, whose influence was often crucial in any aviation matter, even outside his immediate brief.

Brabazon did not consider his first series of meetings to be a success and he therefore reformed the committee in August 1943, renaming it the Second Brabazon Committee. Even now his terms of reference were far from explicit and he himself saw his job as securing 'the best and quickest value . . . that can be got from the diversion of a small percentage of design support now.' Unfortunately there were many who did not see it that way and little enthusiasm was engendered when the committee's report and recommendations were eventually published. In the meantime, it is not unfair to say that the Government did its best to close down the Brabazon Committee as soon as possible, but not before some crucial decisions had been taken.

The original committee recommended five types of aeroplane which it wished to see built and the reformed committee extended these to seven. Even these would 'tend to become obsolete quite quickly in view of the revolutionary aeronautical developments now in sight'. The aircraft so recommended in order of priority were: Brabazon Type I – an airliner capable of a non-stop crossing of the Atlantic from London to New York. This became the Bristol Type 167 Brabazon I. This was to be followed by Brabazon Type III, a smaller Atlantic machine which would eventually become the Bristol Type 175 Britannia.

The Brabazon Type II was for a medium-range machine which eventually split into IIa, the twin piston-engined Ambassador and IIb, the turbo-prop Vickers Viscount.

Brabazon Type IV was a 500mph jet which became the de Havilland Comet. Finally, Brabazon Type V again became two small passenger transports, the Va as the 14-seat Miles Marathon and the Vb, the eight-seat de Havilland Dove.

In view of the fact that Brabazon and his committee spent little or no time in considering the commercial performance of its proposed machines, it is remarkable that any of the aircraft were indeed profitable, as indeed was the Viscount. This machine owed far more to the design genius of George Edwards and his team at Weybridge than it did to the Brabazon Committee.

Lord Brabazon made his first report to the cabinet on 9th February, 1943 and recommended that the large Brabazon Type I should be given priority in design and production, as only thus would the US monopoly be broken. Events now began to fall into place, because earlier in the year on 14th January, Lord Beaverbrook had ordered a meeting to consider the development of a large civil transport plane. Originally, the Bristol company had been excluded from this gathering, but Leslie Frise protested and he attended with a proposal for a 5,000-mile range aircraft based on the 100-ton bomber.

It is interesting to speculate how influential Beaverbrook was in cabinet over the decision to proceed with the Brabazon I. If the decision to go ahead looks from this distance at least controversial, then the choice of manufacturer appears almost foolhardy.

It was assumed by the industry that such a large project could only be undertaken by a firm experienced in building large-structure machines and that one of the bomber companies would get the contract. However, all the likely firms were heavily committed to war contracts. Hence, it was announced by the Secretary of State for Air, Sir Archibald Sinclair, in the House of Commons on 11th March, 1943, that the contract had been awarded to the Bristol Aeroplane Company, on the condition that other essential war work was not affected. The news was greeted with mixed reactions in the industry, where some, like Peter Masefield, did not believe in the capability of Bristols to carry out the work. Second thoughts prevailed, however. While historians are prepared to credit Frise with the conception of the Brabazon I, there were at Filton two other engineers who were structures experts and who had been working throughout the thirties on the torsion stiffness of cantilever wings. H.J. Pollard headed structural research at Filton for over two decades, while Archibald Russell had begun his studies of flexible structures on the Bristol Bagshot of 1927, an aircraft that suffered aileron reversal with almost fatal results to Captain Uwins and his crew, who was Russell! The result of this work led eventually to the Bristol Bombay, a rugged troop carrier with a 96ft cantilever wing which did sterling service on minimum maintenance in the desert in World War II. So Bristol was better equipped to tackle the Brabazon than appeared on the surface.

In April, Sir Wilfred Freeman sent the official invitation to tender and sought views on the necessary sub-contracts for so large an aircraft. By 29th May, 1943, the Ministry had indicated that it would order two prototype machines and ten production versions, although for the present only materials for the prototypes were to be placed on order.

After the air raid on the Filton works in September, 1940, the drawing offices were dispersed to a variety of sites around the city in order to reduce vulnerability in case of future raids. The RAF was ready for any further attempt and the next Luftwaffe sortie, two days later, was dispatched with relative ease by a Polish Hurricane squadron based at Filton. Neither the Filton nor the Patchway site

35

Archibald E. Russell (1904–1996), chief designer of the Bristol Aeroplane Company, as he was at the time of the Brabazon first flight. A graduate of Bristol University, he was made Doctor of Science in 1951, CBE in 1954, FRS in 1970 and knighted in 1972. He would later give his leadership to the Britannia and Concorde programmes.

suffered further bomb damage during the war, but the design offices remained dispersed. The main drawing office for Blenheim, Beaufighter and Beaufort ended up in the Walton Park Hotel at Clevedon, while other projects found space in the tea-rooms at Bristol Zoo.

Among the requisitioned premises for design work was Ivor House in Clifton, Bristol, a large private mansion that dated from Victorian times and was located by The Glen, a well known Bristol landmark that then contained a dance hall but today houses a private hospital.

It was here at Ivor House that the preliminary work on the Brabazon design began to take shape in the summer of 1943. The team began with the studies of the 100-ton bomber, but it soon became obvious that no one had a clear idea of the type of design that was required. Bearing in mind that the bomber was specified to do a round bombing trip from Canada to a Hitler-occupied Europe, the planned ranges were immense but the BOAC representative pointed out glumly that no passenger was likely to endure more than 18 continuous hours in the air. The airline was also specifying that it needed 270 cubic feet per passenger. As early plans allowed for 80 passengers in sleeping berths or 150 in day seats, the pressure towards a very large aeroplane grew, and a fuselage diameter of 25ft was soon being schemed. By mid-summer of that year the Second Brabazon Committee was prepared to recommend the Bristol proposal for a machine of 250,000lb. all up weight with room for 50 passengers. This was supported by a somewhat reluctant BOAC which would have been happy with 25 passengers.

So it became clear very early on that a huge aircraft was being schemed. It would certainly be the largest civil land plane yet built and rivalled for size the big American bomber, the Convair B46, the machine that would eventually be called the Peacemaker.

Work proceeded throughout the autumn and winter of 1943 and into the spring of 1944 but the issue of the first working drawings was still over a year away. Problems abounded, one of the most prominent being the site on which the aircraft was to be built and the size and strength of runway required to fly it. Then there was the whole question of type and size of power plant needed by the monster and the installation required.

One thing was certain. There was nowhere at Filton or anywhere else owned by Bristol that would house a completed Brabazon with its 230ft span. New buildings of appropriate size would be essential to the success of the project. Then again the main runway at Filton had been built for smaller aircraft and moreover was now bounded by the first stage of the dual carriageway Bristol by-pass road, destined in due course to take the A38 trunk road around the city. Expansion to the east was blocked by the main Gloucester road out of the city. So construction of the airliner at Filton did not appear feasible. Then it was that someone at Ivor House came up with the idea of building the Brabazon at the company's airfield at Weston-super-Mare, where Beaufighters and Tempest IIs were under construction at the firm's Banwell plant. The sheds there would take the 176ft length of the fuselage comfortably and the wings could be added in a new shed to be constructed in time to meet the aircraft programme.

A preliminary survey was planned of the Weston runway, which, in its low lying position, gave good access to the clear skies of the Severn estuary and the Bristol Channel. Almost immediately problems arose, not the least of which was the sandy composition of the soil around Weston. It would highly expensive to strengthen the runway sufficiently to support the weight of the Brabazon with an adequate margin of safety at all-up loading.

The only solution was to return to Filton and expand the main runway there by half its length to the west, destroying the new by-pass and the hamlet of Charlton in the process. This was a controversial decision to say the least, but the requisition of land for state purposes had been a commonplace since 1939. Nevertheless, as the war's end was obviously approaching, the process of acquisition became longer, although there appears to have been no local inquiry, such as would be inevitable today. Recently published local histories suggest that the Charlton issue was, though, fought all the way to Cabinet level in June 1945. If this was so, then this was during the last month of Churchill's term of office, as his government fell on 5th July 1945, to be succeeded by Clem Attlee's Labour administration. The change of power made no difference to the outcome, although full agreement to proceed with the runway was not reached until March 1946, eleven months after the first working drawings had been issued to the workshops. Construction of the first prototype had begun in October 1945 but the procrastination led to the eventual first flight being delayed by almost two years to September 1949.

The required runway was defined as 2750 yards long by 100 yards wide and to make way for it Charlton village was demolished as the runway was extended to the west. To go east would have cut the main A38 trunk road and sealed the city off from the north. Charlton was little more than a hamlet but it possessed a large dairy farm, a well known inn and a number of dwelling houses and cottages. A new estate near the Filton airfield at Patchway was built and the work commenced on 1st April, 1946. Fifty houses were completed by 31st

August that year and the Labour government sent its Minister of Health, Nye Bevan down to open it. Many of the displaced residents were still living there 50 years later.

The exceptional length of the runway was determined by the need for the aeroplane to carry out taxi trials and ground handling tests with a reasonable margin of safety. The designed take-off run was 1000 yards at full load, but the trials demanded that at this point of take off, the flight should be aborted and the machine allowed to slow down and come to rest, braking on the runway. This required at least another 1000 yards plus a safety margin and so 2750 yards was arrived at.

The width of 100 yards is generous by today's standards, as many visiting Airbus or Boeing 747 pilots point out to any Filton personnel prepared to listen. The wheel track dimension of the Brabazon was 55 feet (the Boeing 747 is 67ft 4in.) but again the trials requirement dictated the size. As we will see when we consider the design of the Brabazon, there was much consideration of yaw in crosswinds, when a pilot would be required to hold the machine on line as it landed, so it appears that adequate space was planned for this manoeuvre. So the existing Filton runway was extended from 1500 to 2750 yards and widened from 50 to 100 yards. A turning circle of 200 yards diameter was added at each end, to allow the aircraft a turning run, again with adequate safety limits.

The runway designers calculated that the runway would have to cope with loads of 300,000lbs (150 tons) or a margin of above 75 tons per undercarriage leg. This needed a two-foot layer of hardcore over which was laid a further 1ft 8ins of concrete granite aggregate.

The leading British civil engineering company, John Laing and Company Ltd, won the contract which by now had expanded to cover taxiways from the proposed hangar on the south side of the airfield, crossing the Great Western Railway line to Avonmouth by means of a level crossing which was guarded by a large pair of automatic gates.

Laing's began the construction of the runway in September 1946. The whole contract was finished by April 1948 and appears to have proceeded to programme. Certainly, sufficient lengths of taxiway were ready in time for the move of the first fuselage into the Assembly Hall East Bay by September 1947.

Having put the plans for the runway into place, there was the major problem of where the major components of the airframe would be assembled. If the ultimate aim of ten machines in service was to be attained, then a shed capable of taking at least six, and possibly eight, airframes would be required. A decision

39

The Assembly Hall under construction in 1946. Note the steam roller and the huge pile of gravel for the apron.

40

The Assembly Hall as completed.

An aerial view of the newly built runway. The site of the hamlet of Charlton and the Carpenter's Arms Inn lies under the end nearest the camera. At 2,725 yards long and 100 yards wide, it remains one of the longest in the world.

was taken to build such a shed and, in the meanwhile, the basic airframe and wings would be built alongside each other in the No.2 Flight Shed located at the bottom of Filton hill, on which the main factory was located. The erecting hall at Filton was certainly large enough for the Brabazon fuselage to be erected there but the road to the proposed Assembly Hall on the airfield was narrow, confined and ran down a hill. Although quite able to take Beaufighters, Blenheims and Buckinghams, it was far too dangerous to consider using it to move the Brab. Hence the decision to use No.2 Flight Shed, which was just long enough to take the 176ft long fuselage of the Brab, with a clearance of five feet at either end. The 100ft span inner wing could be built as an integral part of the structure as also could the 55ft span tailplane. There was sufficient room to construct the pair of outer wings alongside, although the removal of the fuselage was likely to be tricky with such tight limits. Much later on, this same shed would be used by the company to build the all-stainless steel Type 188 research aircraft, and the same group of sheds housed the mock-up of the SST Concorde airliner.

While the initial layouts were being schemed for the building plan, the first thoughts on the design of the new Assembly Hall were taking shape among the company's small team of architects on Rodney Hill, led by the Chief Architect, Eric Ross. It says much for the magnitude of the development work undertaken by the Bristol Aeroplane Company in those years, that it was able to afford its own architectural department. Brian Colquhoun and Partners were engaged as consulting engineers to the project. The design of the Assembly Hall was largely completed and a working model available by June 1946, and the contract was let to the civil engineers, Sir Alfred McAlpine and Son Ltd. The contract for the gantry cranes went to George W. King Ltd., of Hitchin, Hertfordshire.

Building started in the autumn of 1946 and the magnitude of the shed's dimensions became apparent. The front of the building spread over 1052 feet, split into three equal bays which rose 117 feet in height. The East and West bays were 260 feet deep, while the much larger centre bay extended to 410 feet, intended as it was to contain the assembly line for the Brabazon Mk.II. The total area was approaching seven acres or 290,000 sqare feet. Access for aircraft was by six folding doors, two to each bay and driven by six 5hp electric motors to move the total 220 tons weight of doors.

Immediately outside the building, a 6½ acre concrete apron was levelled into the side of Filton Hill, giving an aircraft handling facility that has since been in constant use for half a century.

43

The very bad winter of January–March 1947 caused the work to be suspended. It was a severe set back to the programme. Only the East Bay was complete by October 1947, ready to receive Brabazon I and nearly a year would pass before the building was completed. By then the Brabazon programme was well behind schedule and so the new West Bay was leased on a temporary basis to house the Constellations and Stratocruisers of BOAC's Atlantic Division.

All this time, the design and construction of the first Brabazon prototype had been proceeding in No.2 Flight Shed, while across the road at Patchway, development of power plants for both marks had begun. A large programme of tests and mock-ups was also underway.

Lord Brabazon's work, and that of his committee, was now done and the committee did not sit beyond 1945. Brabazon's final job in British aviation was Chairman of the Air Registration Board and he was made a Knight Grand Cross of the Order of the British Empire in 1953, when he was sixty-nine. His taste for adventure drove him to make the Cresta run in his seventies and he continued to play golf up to his death in 1964 at the age of 80. Few have served their country more selflessly or with greater devotion to the public good than the first Baron Brabazon of Tara. From his early days as a pioneer pilot, through his service in aerial operations in World War I, where he won the MC, and on to his entry into Parliament where he served many years as a close colleague of Churchill, his one abiding aim was the promotion of Britain to a leading place in the air. It is ironic that the big aeroplane by which he is now chiefly remembered was largely a failure, while two others also recommended by him became the Viscount and Britannia.

FOUR

Construction – In a tin shed at Filton

'The new aeroplane . . . we were about to start would have a wingspan more than three times greater and a weight seven times greater than the largest aeroplane we had worked on before.'

Sir Archibald Russell, A Span of Wings

The airliner that eventually emerged as The Bristol Type 167 Brabazon I owed much of its design conception to the advice given to Leslie Frise by two executives of BOAC, Alan Campbell Orde and Clifford Jackson. Campbell Orde was an original member of Brabazon's committee and it is he who has been identified with the decision to give the Brabazon the luxury quality standards that had existed in the Short Empire flying boats. This even extended to grouping passengers in small cabins each with a capacity of six, spread down the length of the fuselage.

The next big factor to determine Brabazon's design was the requirement to provide a non-stop service between London and New York. When head winds and diversion airfields were included in the calculations, it was seen that a still air range of some 5,500 miles would be required. Bristol had also been awarded the contract for engine design and the most powerful type that Patchway had available was the 2,500hp Bristol Centaurus, a large radial currently being flown in Tempest fighters. There was no gas turbine design likely to be ready until the early fifties and this meant that the first Brabazon would require at least eight Centaurus engines to provide sufficient power to meet speed and range requirements. This was the same arrangement that had been offered for the proposed Bristol 100-ton bomber in 1942 and a certain amount of draft design work was thus available for modification into the airliner proposals.

The project team at Ivor House by now included some of Bristol's rising design stars, among them David Farrar (later of Guided Weapon fame), Barry Laight (who went on to design the Blackburn Buccaneer) and Bill Strang (who headed the British side of Concorde design). The first manufacturing drawings were available to the shops by April 1945. By this time, a full scale mock-up was under construction in the Experimental Department shed at the top of Filton Hill, although all mock-ups would be moved much later, in 1950, to the West Bay of the Assembly Hall when that building was complete.

The summer of 1945 saw the floor of No.2 Flight Shed being cleared to receive the first jigs for construction of the 16ft 9in diameter fuselage, stretching over a length of 177 feet. No.2 Flight Shed had (and still has) an overall length of 280 feet but indoor structure and door bays substantially reduced the available working length.

By now some very significant changes had been made from the 100-ton bomber. The vee tail had been replaced with an orthodox single fin and rudder, the engines turned to face forward rather than pusher, and actually mounted ahead of the front spar, and the undercarriage track reduced from 94 feet to 55 feet, in order to limit runway and taxi-track needs.

Another major advance in aircraft practice concerned the adoption of power-assisted controls for all flying control surfaces. These were hydraulic powered and were in fact duplicated to avoid control immobility if the first system were to fail at any time. Even so, the ministry officials concerned with flight safety required the first aircraft to carry lead mass balances on all major control surfaces during its flying career. These mass balances affected the otherwise clean, sleek appearance of the Brabazon's streamlined hull, but even so the type remains one of the best looking aircraft ever to fly.

Detail manufacture began as soon as the first drawings were issued in April 1945 and assembly work followed as soon as the jigs had been erected. There were five major jigs in all: the fuselage and 110ft 6in inner wing, port and starboard outer wings, fin and tailplane. As the limiting height of the flight shed was only 28 feet, the fin was built in horizontal position and lifted into position when the aircraft was finally located in the assembly hall. The tailplane was assembled on to the fuselage in late 1946, and this was done in No.2 Flight Shed, despite the space limitations.

It has often been said that the Brabazon was built more in the fashion of a ship than an aeroplane, and as far as the erection of her frames goes, this is an apt comment. Photographs taken at the time, and still in the Filton archives,

The wooden mock-up of the Brabazon under construction in the Experimental Shop at Filton on 17th January, 1946.

Initial erection of mainframes in No.2 Flight Shed on 25th February, 1946. In the foreground, frame segments await assembly.

Three weeks later, on 18th March, 1946, the fitting of stringers is well under way.

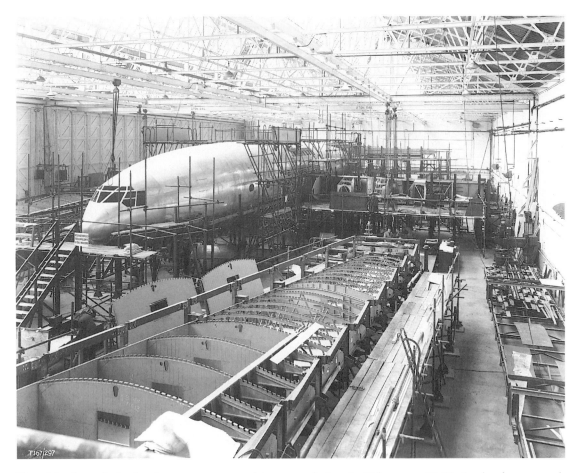

The skinning of the fuselage was approaching completion in February, 1947. In the foreground, the outer wings were taking shape.

show that all the frames were erected first. Here the comparison with a shipyard ends, as the fuselage was a monocoque design, covered with stressed aluminium alloy skins of appropriate gauge according to the location in the structure. The frames were of rolled channel section and joined together with Z-section stringers to form the basis frame of the fuselage over which the skins were finally rivetted.

In addition to the frames and stringers, the fuselage was strengthened by three main logerons which ran fore to aft. One ran along the top of the fuselage, while the two others were fitted to run either side of the lower fuselage. The skin was re-inforced around the periphery of all hatches, doors and windows. The cabin windscreen was of a single pre-fabricated frame.

Although commonplace today, stress skin construction in the mid-forties was a technique that was in its infancy on both sides of the Atlantic. Cabin pressurisation had been introduced by Boeing in its Stratoliner of 1938 and stress skin construction was the best way of getting the strength that pressurisation demanded. The Brabazon design was advanced for its day and comprised vertical butt joints where the skins met in that plane while horizontal joins overlapped. Skins of 14 gauge were used in the central section, tapering off to 16 gauge and then 18 gauge as the nose and tail sections were reached. The fuselage skinning was largely complete by July, 1946, a date well behind the initial programme for two very good reasons.

The first delay arose from many of the skins coming in well over weight. Weight control is mandatory in all aircraft construction and the Brabazon was no exception, so that when skins were found to be overweight, a major investigation was called for. The cause of the problem was tracked down to flexing of the rolls used on the light alloy sheets in the rolling mill. Hence the sheets were of correct thickness at the edges but too thick in the middle, and therefore too heavy. Adjustment of the rolling process cured the problem but delay occurred.

The other delay was the decision of Russell and his team to improve the strength of the fuselage by cleating the stringers to the frames, whereas before the stringers were free to move. This gave a much stronger fuselage, but entailed more delay.

The delays to the assembly programme were serious and caused the forecast date for the first flight to be put back from April 1947 to August 1948.

The centre wing box was built concurrently and integrally with the main fuselage, and in the same set of jigs. The construction was in the classic wing form of vertical front and rear spars made up of sheet webs placed between spar

51

booms. These spar booms were made up from rolled section and braced at critical points around the engine bearers by tubular steel struts. At its widest point, the front spar was 6ft 6in in height and nearly twice the height of the rear spar.

The centre section skins were attached to lateral stringers and were among the thickest on the aircraft, being $\frac{3}{16}$ inch in width. There was strong reinforcing around all breaks in the structure, particularly in the area of the wheel bays.

Attached forward of the front spar were the box girder bearings for the engine mountings. Eventually, each engine of the pair would be hung either side of the box and the joint drive gear box mounted on the front of the box. The rear completed the wing structure aft where the flaps when fitted would complete the wing outline. Finally, the leading edges were added by enclosing D frames with stringers and skins and mounting these forward of the front spar, leaving the appropriate spaces where cowlings were to be mounted later.

A separate piece of centre wing structure was built at the same time as work commenced on the wing box. By the spring of 1946, sufficient fuselage structure was in position to allow the wing to be secured in place and both spars were in place by August, all ready for skinning. This task was completed by January, 1947, and the engine mountings went in during the summer of 1947. An additional piece of wing box, 21ft in length, was supplied to the Engine Division test beds at Patchway to replace the crude RSJ steel girder test rig of which the first pairs of engines had been tested to date.

Work did not begin on the construction of the outer wings until January 1947, by which time the tailplane had already been mounted on the rear fuselage. The pair of outer wings were built in opposite hand jigs alongside the fuselage in No. 2 Flight Shed and were of conventional box girder shape, made up of front and rear spars joined with ribs, stringers and skins. Inner bulkheads protected the fuel tanks which were carried in the inner wings and the finalisation of the fuel system design may have been the cause of the late start of wing construction. However, the work went ahead at a pace and the wings were ready by September. To handle the wings, two special trolleys were ordered from Follands of Hamble, who designed and delivered these in time for the impending move to the Assembly Hall.

Follands also won the contract to build the flying control surfaces. These were assembled at Hamble and consisted of two 42ft ailerons, elevators (75ft. over-all), flaps and 50ft rudder.

So construction proceeded through 1946 and 1947 while Laings struggled to make up the lost time to the Assembly Hall programme caused by the bad winter of 1947. By the end of September, 1947, the fuselage and centre wings were ready for transfer to the Assembly Hall, the east bay of which was just about complete, although much finishing work remained to be done, including the roofs of the centre and west bays.

The move on 4th October, 1947 was named 'Operation Shoehorn' after the tight clearances required to move the aircraft. The floor area around the main jigs was cleared and the airframe raised on jacks to allow the fitting of a dummy tricycle under-carriage. The Brab was lowered onto this after the full removal of the jigs. A 3-ton tractor was attached by tow-bar to the stern, and as planned, the big structure was eased out stern first as the nose revolved towards the rear wall of the hangar. The tail plane cleared the shed doors by 2ft 6in, while the nose eased past the rear wall with 1ft 3ins to spare. The engineers of the Factory Layout Section later claimed that these figures were exactly as planned.

Once the machine was clear of the Flight Shed, the tractor commenced the short quarter mile journey to the awaiting east bay of the Assembly Hall, accompanied by a triumphant group of employees who watched while the Brabazon I was carefully manoeuvred into her new home. The outer wings followed and these were lined up in position alongside the centre wing, thus giving for the first time some impression of the true size of the monster aircraft.

The company had arranged with the Ministry of Supply, who were now the aircraft's owners, for a naming ceremony to be held. This was to be done by the Rt. Hon. John Wilmot, M.P., Minister of Supply on 14th October, 1947. Like so many well regulated plans that sometimes go astray, this one gave rise to one of Britain's enduring political legends. The Prime Minister of the day, Clement Attlee, sent for Wilmot on the day before the naming ceremony and sacked him from the government. When Wilmot asked the reason, Attlee took his pipe from his mouth and uttered the immortal line: 'Sorry, not up to it. Good morning!'

So it was the Technical Controller at the Ministry, Air Marshal Sir Alec Coryton, who stood in and named the Brabazon, in the presence of Lord Brabazon of Tara and the Lord Mayor of Bristol. The occasion was presided over by Bristol's rising star, Reginald Verdon Smith who was now joint assistant managing director, sharing the post with his cousin George White, grandson of the founder. The Lord Mayor said how proud Bristol was of the company, and Lord Brabazon said how proud he was that the aircraft carried his name, although no one had sought his permission. The crowd dispersed and the final assembly began.

On the move for the first time on 4th October, 1947 at the start of Operation Shoehorn.

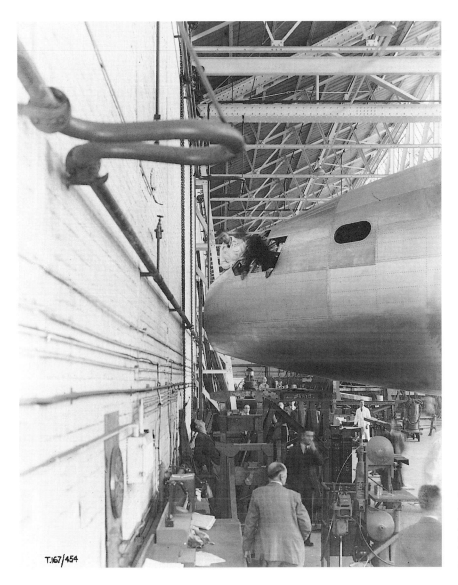

T.167/454

A near thing as the nose eases past the rear wall of No.2 Flight Shed with 1ft 3in to spare!

55

Leaving No.2 Flight Shed backwards as Operation Shoehorn is concluded.

FIVE

Tests and trials

'Our big aeroplane disappeared into the sky
and all was well.'

Sir Archibald Russell, A Span of Wings

By the time of the naming ceremony of the Brabazon I in October 1947, Leslie Frise had resigned his post as Chief Engineer of the Bristol Aeroplane Company and taken up the position of Chief Designer of Hunting Percival Ltd. of Luton, Bedfordshire. Frise had been appointed to Barnwell's job following the latter's death in an aircraft accident in 1938 and had seen the difficult war years through at Filton. Echoing Fedden, he claimed never to have had an easy relationship with the Bristol board. Archibald Russell relates in his autobiography how Frise told him, 'They've been gunning for me for some time.' Russell was now indisputably Chief Designer, a post from which he led the Bristol technical effort with flare and ingenuity, and also with much good humour. He would eventually lead the design teams that produced the Concorde SST airliner, one of the great engineering achievements of the twentieth century.

Just prior to his departure from Filton, Leslie Frise had been heard to criticise the decision to use the Bristol Centaurus engine in the Brabazon, a plan formulated in 1944 and based on the scheme to use coupled pairs of Centaurus in the 100-ton bomber. Much development and test-bed work was needed to produce this motor, and Frise pondered that the effort expended would have been better used in going straight for the more powerful Proteus gas turbine, which had been specified for the Mark II Brabazon and succeeding production aircraft. Frise may well have been right, as the later troubles with the Proteus delayed the Brabazon II, the Saunders Roe Princess giant flying boat and the early version of the Bristol Britannia, nearly bringing down the Bristol company in the process.

The use of the Centaurus, requiring so many modifications, clearly led to delay but the big radial was certainly tried and tested, while no delivery date was available for the Proteus. The Centaurus was Fedden's greatest engine and had been type tested as long ago as 1938. It had powered some of the RAF's most successful warplanes and was rated at the war's end as Britain's most powerful aero-engine.

The Centaurus XX, as specified for the Brabazon, was the Type 57 version coupled in a pair and driving contra-rotating airscrews by diagonal shafts geared to prop shafts inter-rotating with each other. The basic engine was an eighteen-cylinder sleeve valve two-row aircooled radial with 7in stroke, a bore of 5.75in and a swept volume of 3,270 cu.in., the equivalent of 53.6 litres cubic capacity. Each motor developed 2,520hp at 2,700 revs using 100 octane fuel at sea level, although power fell away as altitude increased. The Centaurus had the reputation of being a very rugged engine which could take considerable punishment in action. However, the driving gear to the propellers had to be designed from scratch, manufactured, strength tested, assembled, test run and finally type tested to ARB standards before being allowed into a flying aeroplane. In the event, each engine was coupled to its own airscrew, each pair of shafts being co-axial and contra-rotating. Reduction gearboxes, engine mountings, accessory drives and cooling systems all had to be supplied: an extremely lengthy and expensive operation when applied to a one-off aeroplane.

The Engine Division used two test rigs for the engines and gearboxes. The first was commissioned in April 1946 and was quite a simple affair made up of steel RSJ girders. Later that year in November, the 21ft section of inner wing was delivered and testing transferred to that, where vibration tests were also possible.

Once the first sets of gearboxes were up and running, testing went ahead fairly smoothly, and by February 1948 a total of 616 hours running had been achieved. The engines for Brab I had been delivered to the Assembly Hall by this time. During the continuous test running – much of it at night – the residents of Filton and Patchway became accustomed to the incessant drone that pervaded the air of the north Bristol area. There were few public protests, as most people were only too aware of the income that the Filton works brought to the area. Attitudes have changed: contrast their passive response with the well organised opposition to the proposed development of Filton as a civil airport fifty years later. Engine test running concluded in April 1949 with the Arb 150-hour type test run to clear the engine installation for civil aircraft flying. The test programme had lasted 3125 hours of development running.

A Bristol Centaurus engine now preserved by the Rolls-Royce Heritage Trust in the Bristol Industrial Museum. Eighteen-cylinder, sleeve valve, it delivered 2,190 hp at 5,000ft and eight were used to drive the Brabazon I. (courtesy: Bristol City Council).

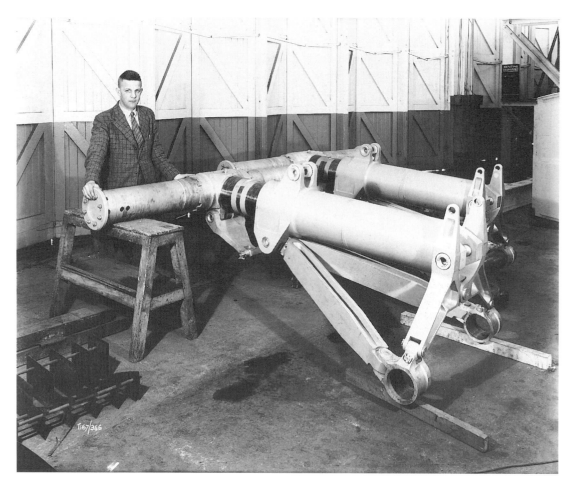

Fred Harpur, superintendent, with the first set of main undercarriage legs delivered from Dowtys in April, 1947.

Attaching the towing arm.

Preparing to fit a main wheel to its axle.

A pair of port main wheels as supplied by Dunlop, 6th January, 1949. These were later replaced by 4-wheel bogies.

As final development programmes approached completion and with the final assembly well under way, the design team could look back on a series of test rigs and specimens that far outstripped any previous project. As well as the engine test rigs, a half scale model was built, a structural test piece which was erected at the RAE's 'Cathedral' Hangar at Farnborough to carry out loading tests on the main aircraft structure. Loads were calculated to simulate those likely to be experienced in full size conditions, the span still being 115ft. The Farnborough tests on the half scale model continued throughout 1946 and proved their worth when part of the inner wing actually failed under test. Redesign was carried out and eventually clearance of the structure was given.

No metal fatigue testing was carried out on the Brabazon structure rigs. The problem was little understood, and not until the Comet disasters of 1954 would a full study of metal fatigue be carried out and every aircraft be preceded by a full scale test rig which was kept 'flying' several hundred hours ahead of the oldest flying specimen. Harmonics and vibration were subjects that were thoroughly understood, however, and their impact on a large aircraft were the subject of much research using a 20th scale test specimen built for the purpose. This allowed early checks on resonance, for, although the completed airplane would undergo full resonance tests, it was too late then to make any major changes.

All cockpit and cabin layouts were first tried out on the full scale wooden mock-up which was constructed in the Filton Experimental Department by a large team of carpenters, an important trade in the aircraft industry of those days. The flight deck was 'mocked up' for a crew of six: two pilots, two flight engineers, navigator and radio operator. Behind the crew positions was the crew rest-room, and behind that the entry lobby. There followed a series of passenger lounges which were altered in design as BOAC requirements dictated. The mock-up was made to high standards, particularly the seating, and this became a standard works tour for visiting VIPs from the Government, Ministry of Supply, service chiefs and airline executives who streamed to Filton in their hundreds for an inspection. Later in its career, when the centre bay of the hangar was ready, the mock-up was moved there alongside the fuselage of the Brabazon II.

By the autumn of 1947, the programme of test rigs which allowed development and clearance of the various flight systems was largely complete. This huge volume of work had readied the systems for installation and so avoided a large programme of ground running of the actual airplane itself.

A large hydraulic rig was constructed in the corner of the Experimental Shop near the mock-up. It included the landing gear, with the nose wheel steering gear

T.167/459

Ready for the tow to the east bay of the new Assembly Hall. Note the twin cab towing tractor and towing arm attached. The mass balance arms are already in position on the tailplane.

Safe in a bleak, barely completed east bay, on 4th October, 1947. The starboard outer wing has arrived as well.

The starboard wing on its Folland-built trolley leaving No.2 Flight Shed. The figure in the centre is the Brab.I superintendent, Fred Harpur, well known in Bristol rugby circles.

The naming ceremony on 8th October, 1947. The platform party is (l. to r.): unknown, the Lord Mayor of Bristol, Alderman Robert Lyne, Lord Brabazon of Tara, Mr. W. Reginald Verdon Smith, asst. joint managing director and Air-Marshal Sir Alec Coryton who performed the ceremony.

Assembling the fin to the aircraft: November 1947.

incorporated, the flap controls and all the units for the power-operated controls which Russell had specified for the first time in a British design. Each of the hydraulic control units was test run for a total of 500 hours, after which the elevator unit was flight tested in an Avro Lancaster for a total of 50 hours flight time. The main feature of the power controls was that each unit contained two actuators, duplicating the same movement so that back up was available in case of failure.

Two other examples of systems being tested in other aircraft were the de-icing system, carried aloft in a Bristol Buckingham, and the gust alleviator system which was flight tested in another Lancaster. Gusts at altitude are a hazard to every large aircraft and a gust sensing vane was mounted on the port side of the cockpit, 80ft ahead of the ailerons. The vane had an airfoil section which signalled the presence of gusts by an electrical link to the aileron controls. Lift was shed by raising the ailerons in an upgust, and vice-versa in downgusts. The gust alleviator vane was a prominent feature of the first Brabazon and caused much comment in the technical press of the time. The engine power available in the first machine limited it to a cruising speed of 250mph at 25,000 ft and at such speeds, the gust limitation sought by the Ministry authorities was achievable. It was planned, however, that the Proteus-powered second aircraft and subsequent machines would cruise at 330mph at 35,000 ft. Here gust warning and automatic trimming was considered essential and it is now history that the problem was never satisfactorily resolved. This was to be one of the prime causes for the cancellation of the project in 1953.

Final assembly proceeded throughout the winter of 1947 and into the spring of 1948. During this time the landing gear was fitted and the aircraft jacked so that early trials could be attempted. The landing gear was made and supplied by the well tried Cheltenham firm of Dowty Ltd., and carried eight main wheels disposed in pairs on either side of each main undercarriage leg, and two nose-wheels, one on either side of the nose-leg. The sets of tyres were supplied by Dunlop and the eight main wheels were considered a temporary safety measure, after which the second aircraft would fly on four only.

After the fitting of the outer wings to the centre wing in November, 1947, the installation of the fuel system could proceed. The first proposal was to use integral fuel tanks, but this proved too advanced for the Ministry of Supply. Standard flexible bags were specified instead, and the entire outer wings used for the purpose, while integral tanks were postponed to the second aircraft. This was probably wise, because although integral tanks are commonplace today,

70

sealing techniques in the forties left much to be desired and more delays could have been incurred. Twenty eight bag tanks in all, fourteen in each outer wing, were installed, giving a total fuel capacity of 13,650 imperial gallons, of which only 150 gallons were unusable. The fuel was fed by a gravity system into under-wing collector boxes and hence pumped into the engine, de-icing and cabin heater systems.

Early on in the project, Archibald Russell and his team recognised that the existing practice of using DC electrical systems in aircraft would not provide the power demanded by the many advanced systems to be installed in the Brabazon. Leading the thinking here was Bill Irens, the company's electrical engineer, who later went on to be chairman of the South Western Electricity Board, where he pioneered gas turbines for electricity generation. Power was supplied by six engine-driven 30 kva alternators built by Rotax Ltd and delivering a three-phase supply of 208 volts. A rectified DC supply of 28 volts was also available and, with the usual 'belt and braces' approach to Brabazon systems, two banks of batteries were available for emergencies at 23 mins. at 300 amps.

As 1948 proceeded, so the final touches to the assembled aircraft took place. The fin had been added soon after the move to the Assembly Hall, and in February 1948 the huge rudder was set in place and connected up to the control systems, as were the flaps, ailerons and elevators. The propellor shaft mountings went in the same month and the first deliveries of the banks of instrumentation began to arrive at the Assembly Hall. The propellors were delivered and fitted by Rotol in May, 1948.

The Brabazon was later recorded as the 'most instrumented aircraft ever to fly'. There are good grounds for this claim, as the machine was so large that it had plenty of space to carry instrumentation for everything that needed to be instrumented. The crew members each had a full set of instruments for their particular disciplines and these were set up in the cockpit and crew stations as originally planned on the mock-up.

By 1948, the Proteus gas turbine engine was running well behind programme, apart from being in deep technical trouble, and the original decision to use the first aircraft as a test machine appeared to be well justified. However, the delay allowed the time to cram the first aircraft full of instrumentation. This was mounted on twelve auto observer panels, each fitted with an automatic camera which recorded all instrument readings on cine film. As some 1,100 dials in all had to be filmed, the amount of information obtained was immense and took a great deal of time to analyse.

71

After the naming ceremony, employees crowd round the new monster to get a good view.

The aircraft at the fuelling point on 18th August, 1948, when flow checks were commenced. Work is still proceeding on the assembly hall and the Avro Lancaster used to flight test the power controls rests on the apron.

Pressure fuelling under way on 15th November, 1948. The figure in the picture is Frank Chard, who was production manager of the Brabazon project in its later years.

The engine installation of eight Centaurus 18-cylinder radials of 2,190hp each, as seen from the hangar roof.

Close-up of the completed engine bay structure viewed from the hangar roof, 15th November, 1948.

Engine running trials underway on 19th November, 1948. This picture gives a good impression of the 16ft diameter Rotol contra-rotating propellers.

T.167/763

Resonance testing proceeding on 5th December, 1948. The aircraft is supported on high pressure rubber air bags.

The twelves AOPs, as they were known, were allocated to systems as follows:

1. Aircraft performance
2. Services e.g. hydraulics, electrics ops
3. Power controls
4. Engine temperatures
5. Engine cooling systems
6. Oil temperatures
7. Propellers
8. Hydraulic oil temperatures
9. Alternator systems
10. Pressurisation and air systems
11. De-icing systems
12. Air flows and dynamics

The chief flight test observer had overall control of the cameras, but observers could take individual readings.

During this summer of 1948, final checks were made of the pressurisation system, which had been developed on the pressure test specimen built earlier, 40ft long and representing the nose assembly. Two cabin blowers designed by Godfrey Ltd were fitted, one to each inboard engine assembly, and these delivered 5½lb per sq.in. so as to give a cabin altitude of 8,000 ft when the actual altitude was 25,000 ft. The whole fuselage was pressurised except for short portions of the nose and tail; this included the inner wing roots and the nose-wheel bay, both of which gave trouble before satisfactory results were achieved.

Fuel calibration checks were carried out in August 1948 when the aircraft was fuelled up for the first time, using the newly installed fuel station at the rear of the hangar. Fuel flow tests followed in November to check fuel pressures to all engines, while in the same month the long awaited resonance testing began. This was looked upon as the last stage before engine ground running and the approach to flight testing began.

During the last weeks of December, 1948, the engines were ground run for an initial total of 20 hours over a full range of revs up to 2,700rpm and delivering 20,000hp. More ground running was done in 1949, while all systems were tested.

In early 1949, the Brabazon was moved to the centre bay while a weighbridge was installed in the floor of the west bay by Salters of West Bromwich, aided by W.T. Avery Ltd. This installation measured the weight on each oleo leg of the undercarriage and allowed the all-up weights of the aircraft to be calculated.

When the results were disclosed, it appeared that the empty weight was 169,500lb (75 tons), maximum landing weight was 240,000lb (107 tons), fuel load 100,000lb (45 tons), and payload was 20,000lb (9 tons). All this gave a calculated range of 5,460 miles, cruising at 250mph while at 25,000 feet. The time to prove the test results in flight trials was approaching.

79

Bristol's chief test pilot was A.J. Pegg, known to all as 'Bill' and he had been with the company as deputy to the great Cyril Uwins since 1935. Uwins had flown his last of many prototypes on 2nd December 1945, the Type 170 Freighter, and the following year had handed over the job to Bill Pegg. The Brabazon was to be Pegg's first flight of a company prototype and none could be more calculated to arouse greater public interest. To prepare for the task, Pegg spent many hours 'getting the feel' of the aircraft controls on the appropriate tests rigs. Some of these trials were not without incident. One day Pegg selected flaps down, only to be nonplussed as the flap promptly went up! He was assured that it would not happen on the real thing. The only similar sized aircraft in existence were an American bomber and two huge flying boats. Of the flying boats, the British Saro Princess would not be ready until 1952, while the second, the vast wooden Hughes H2 Spruce Goose, had already made its only flight of one mile in the hands of its erratic creator, Howard Hughes. The bomber was a better proposition, however, and Pegg spent some weeks in the US in the spring of 1949 as the guest of the Convair company, learning how to handle the big B36, which conveniently had the same 230ft span and the same weight as the Brabazon.

Ground testing proceeded all through the summer of 1949, but now a date was approaching that demanded that the Brabazon take to the air. The Society of British Aircraft Constructors Annual Exhibition and Flying Display at Farnborough was due to open in the first week of September. The show was the industry's shop window, where it could display its achievements to the nation and the world. £12 million of taxpayers' money was being invested in the Brabazon project and many in government felt it was time the taxpayer saw what he and she were getting for their money. A flight over the show would provide just that.

First of all came the taxi-ing trials. The test flight crew was named with Bill Pegg as captain and Walter Gibb as co-pilot. It included Alan Cowan as flight engineer, L.D. Atkinson, chief flight engineer (engines), John Hayman, flight engineer (engines), Ken Fitzgerald, electrical engineer, M.J. Peniston, chief flight test observer with flight test observers Malcolm West, John Sizer and John Cochrane.

On Saturday, 3rd September, the aeroplane was loaded to a gross weight of 190,000lb, including 2,000 gallons of fuel. In an atmosphere of growing excitement, a series of test runs along the runway were carried out at increasing speeds. The nose began to lift at 75 knots or so, at which the throttles were pulled back and the machine slowed down. The crew reported all systems to be functioning normally, and the only snag was the non-function of the nose wheel steering, which was then disconnected. Steering was accomplished by differential use of the main brakes. On completion of the trial runs, the aircraft went on all-night inspection to be readied for the morrow.

All Bristol knew that a flight was expected on Sunday, 4th September and crowds, later estimated at 10,000 people, surrounded the airfield from an early hour. 300 journalists and news cameramen from around the world had been invited. In late morning, the Brab was towed to the east end of the main runway where the motors were started and warmed up. She then taxied along the runway to the famous 'hill' and disappeared from the view of the crowds. At the west end of the runway, she turned eastward into a 7-knot cross-wind from the south east, so this could well be a take off. As she began her run, the Brab was loaded at 210,000lb, with fuel upped to 4,000 gallons. The cross-wind demanded the use of opposite rudder, but Pegg decided to continue, and after a run of 500 yards and at about 75–80 knots, the Brabazon I lifted gracefully into the air. A slight hesitation was all the watching crowd saw of the famous 'nose up' incident described in Chapter 1. As the crowds cheered, the aircraft proceeded on her majestic way to carry out an anti-clockwise circuit of south Gloucestershire, over the Severn estuary and back to Filton at an airspeed of 140 knots and a maximum height of 4,000 feet. Then, after a flight time of 27 minutes, and a landing speed of 88 knots, Pegg brought the Brabazon into a perfect landing using only 600 yards of runway to pull up. It had been a great success. Lord Brabazon, watching from the control tower, echoed the relief of many when he commented, 'I have never seen any trial go off so smoothly'.

Chief test pilot Bill Pegg and chief designer Archibald Russell at Filton for the first flight.

Bill Pegg looking out from the cockpit of the Brabazon Mk I.

The Brabazon design team stand around as A.E. Russell makes a presentation to his right-hand man on the project, Fred Pollicutt.

The author in the cockpit of the Brabazon Mk I at the SBAC show at Farnborough in September 1951. (courtesy: Alf Samuels).

The completed Mk I aircraft outside the Assembly Hall, together with a restored Bristol F2B Fighter of 1916. The Fighter is today in the Shuttleworth Collection.

Preparing for taxi-ing trials at Filton on 3rd September, 1949.

The simple pilot's flight panel on the Brabazon Mk I.

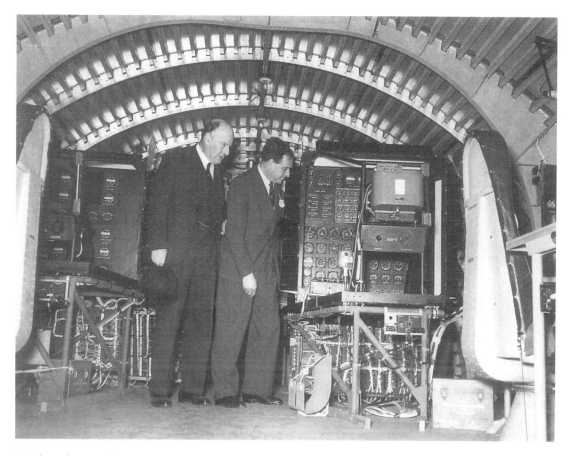

Lord Brabazon of Tara, 1884–1964, Chairman of the Brabazon Committee, and George Strauss, MP., Minister of Supply, inspecting instrumentation stations on board the Brabazon during the flight to Heathrow on 15th June, 1950.

Brabazon Mk I G-AGPW coming into land at Filton after her second flight. The picture has been signed by a number of Bristol test pilots.

Landing at Heathrow, the first away from Filton, on 15th June, 1950.

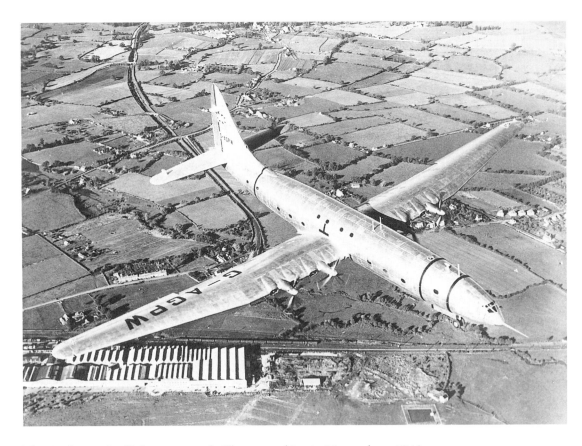

The Brabazon in flight over south Gloucestershire in November, 1949.

In flight accompanied by a Bristol Type 170 Freighter, a 'bread and butter', no frills aeroplane of which 214 were built.

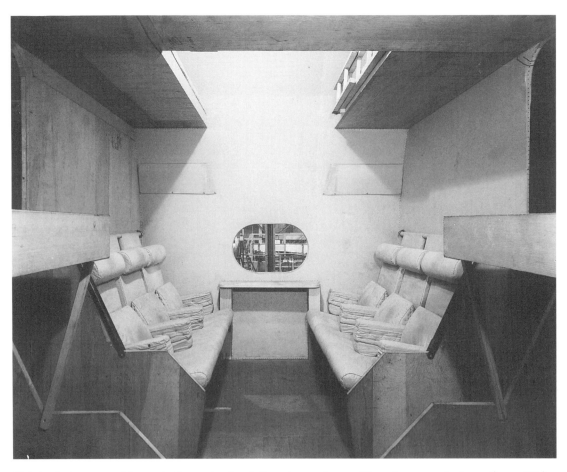

Original six-seat cabin as laid out in the full-scale mock up. The photograph dates from 30th August, 1945 and shows how dated were BOAC's ideas of luxury accommodation.

The VIP lounge fitted to the Brabazon just prior to the Heathrow flight. Passengers never saw such spaciousness again.

Filton staff act as model passengers to demonstrate the space planned aboard the Brabazon. Back row left to right: Jack Longley, senior production engineer, Les Duckett, senior inspector, Fred Harpur, superintendent, Front Row: unknown lady, Frank Chard, production manager and Josie Carter, secretary.

SIX

Meanwhile – In another part of the planet . . .

'The Brabazon was doomed, but its inertia sustained it for another three years. It did, however, initiate a good deal of advanced technology.'

Sir Archibald Russell – A Span of Wings

In the weeks and months following that first flight, the Brabazon I became something of a flying icon to the people of Bristol. Carefully seeking public approval, the directors arranged for parts of the test programme to overfly all the major cities of the United Kingdom. As the flight tests could be carried out almost anywhere, this policy made good sense but at the end of each flight, the Brab returned to Filton. Her engines had a characteristic drone which was instantly recognisable. Pegg and Gibb rarely had flight plans which called for more than 150 knots airspeed, and therefore it was usual for those on the ground to hear her approach long before she hove into view. There were many who held the view that, rather than fly, the Brabazon 'proceeded' and to witness her stately progress was certainly to enhance that view. 'Ah, there goes the Brab!' said everyone in north Bristol as the familiar sound heralded the beginning or end of another test flight.

By the end of January, 1950, fourteen test flights had been completed for a total of 29 hours and an altitude of 10,000ft had been reached. Routine testing of all systems proceeded with few snags. The first major problem – a leak in the hydraulic reservoir system – occurred on the first flight of which Walter Gibb took command, on 15th January, 1950. Without hydraulic oil, there would have to be a belly landing and possible loss of the aircraft, so the flight set to work transferring oil from other systems to the landing gear reservoir. Meanwhile, the aircraft returned to Filton and then circled for two hours while a scheme for landing was worked out. Once the landing gear was down, one leg showed a red light to indicate it was not locked, although looking fine. Gibb eventually made a flapless landing at a higher than usual speed and then abandoned the machine in the middle of the runway, after cutting all power. The cause of the trouble was a hydraulic oil leak in the inner wing and the locking pin of the main undercarriage had not gone fully home.

In February, after a flight of five hours covering 1000 miles, the aircraft made a long programme of stall checks, carried out at the safe altitude of 20,000 feet and at varying positions of aircraft altitude. In later years Walter Gibb was heard to comment that the Brab behaved well in a stall, recovering on her own, after losing perhaps 2,500 feet at most in the stall. The trick was to be strapped in your seat before the stall began, as some unwary crew members discovered the hard way.

Speed trials followed, and by June 1950 the first part of the testing was complete. The aircraft had performed satisfactorily and delivered the perform-ance of speed and height that the Centaurus engine could achieve. A luxury passenger cabin of thirty seats had been installed and a licence to carry limited passenger numbers obtained. On 15th June 1950, the Brab made her first visit to London Heathrow, where she carried out a number of demonstration flights, including one with 20 members of parliament, a number of VIPs and Lord and Lady Brabazon of Tara.

All appeared well on the surface, but behind the scenes, 1950 was to prove a climactic year for the project, and one in which its fate was sealed. The problems were considerable: expensive operating costs, fatigue failure of the engine mounting structure, the failure to deliver the Proteus engine for the Brabazon II and, above all, the ability of the American industry to supply aircraft that would do the same job at half the cost.

The engine issue was soon to the fore. Bristol had entered the jet age by producing two propeller turbines, the Theseus and the Proteus. Archibald Russell has described the Theseus as a dismal failure and he was soon to find out more about the Proteus, too. This engine had been specified for the Brabazon II and the Saro Princess flying boat. The future of both projects therefore turned on the success of the Proteus engine. Its good features were lack of vibration, hence eliminating fatigue, and the ability to deliver power at altitude, high above the gust problem. But there was one basic problem. To reduce the geometric length of the engine, compressor air entered at the rear, travelled forward to the burners and then reversed flow to drive the turbines which in turn drove the props and compressors. This layout was complicated enough to develop and by mid-1950

98

Taking off from Filton on the second flight on 7th September, 1949.

Fly past over Heathrow on 15th June, 1950.

the Proteus was in deep trouble, being 800lb overweight and 1000hp down in power. There was no prospect of its being ready on time for the Brabazon II or the Princess, although the latter was so far into its programme that the ten Proteus engines required for the first machine were eventually delivered.

Here one of the great men of British aviation enters the story. Stanley Hooker was head of gas turbine development at Rolls-Royce, having worked with Whittle on the early turbines, after developing the power output of the famous Merlin. In 1948, he walked out after a clash with the head of Rolls, Lord Hives. Hooker had known Reginald Verdon Smith at Oxford, and when Verdon Smith heard of Hooker's departure from Derby, he immediately offered him a job at Bristol. In 1950, when the trouble with the Proteus became critical, Verdon Smith made Hooker Chief Engineer of Bristol Engines and Hooker set about a complete redesign of the Proteus. In this he was eventually successful, even though late deliveries of the Proteus engine ruined the Britannia project and came near to bringing down the Bristol Aeroplane Company. Only the cool leadership of Reginald Verdon Smith brought the organisation through this severely testing time.

Hooker's redesign was too late for the Brabazon, which all along had been based on faulty commercial estimates, for which BOAC must accept a large share of the blame. The luxury transport concept of the Brabazon had been drawn up on the basis of £400 per hour operating costs, giving a cost of £100 per passenger for a trip to New York, a huge sum for those days. This did not allow for any of the £12 million costs of the project, which included £6 million for the Assembly Hall and runway. The operation was clearly an economic impossibility and the first to point this out were BOAC. In *A Span of Wings*, Archibald Russell admits to having doubts at an early stage but, as he disarmingly says, 'when a customer asks you to design and build a very large aeroplane, you don't discourage him.' But the Brabazon was only one of a number of immediate post-war British airliners which failed this economy test, along with the Avro Tudor series and the H.P. Hermes. The Airspeed Ambassador was hardly more successful, selling only to BEA and one has to look to George Edwards' Vickers Viking to find a British airliner of the time that sold in any worthwhile numbers.

There were good practical reasons for BOAC to hold the views that they did. For much of the war, they had been running their airline with converted bombers, carrying perhaps nine passengers or so. Meanwhile in America, a large proportion of the US war effort had gone into transporting men and supplies by air, and the effort paid off. By the time war with Japan ended in August 1945,

America had three excellent machines in production which had started life as military transports and were now available for civilian use. BOAC were in due course to buy versions of all three and so start the co-operation between Britain's national airline and the American aircraft industry which has lasted without a break to this day.

First in the field was the Douglas DC4, a four-engined update of the durable DC3, and soon to be followed by the DC6 and DC7. Large numbers of surplus DC4s were available and American Airlines opened transatlantic services to Europe with the type in 1946. In 1948, BOAC were given permission to buy a version of the DC4 built by Canadair in Montreal to replace the unsuccessful Tudors and 22 were ordered. BOAC were also allowed to order the other two American machines, the Lockheed Constellation and the Boeing Stratocruiser for its Atlantic services. So when, in 1950, uses were being sought for the Brabazon I, the BOAC fleet consisted of six Stratocruisers, 11 Constellations, 22 Canadairs and, the only British type, 25 Hermes which were to last only two years before being sold on. The supreme irony was that, because the BOAC base at Heathrow was not yet ready, the east bay of the Assembly Hall at Filton was rented to BOAC for maintenance of its Atlantic Division and the Brabazon now had the competition literally on its doorstep. When the proposition came from Lockheed that Bristol build the Constellation under licence at Filton with Centaurus engines, the government of the day banned the scheme on the grounds of dollar saving. It is interesting to speculate on what might have happened if that scheme had gone ahead.

Meanwhile, two schemes for the Brabazon I and another for the Mk.II had been examined and turned down. The first was to attempt a transatlantic flight but the gust problem was considered to make the crossing too dangerous. The second proposal was to use the Brab on the London-Nice service of BEA but this was rejected on the grounds of cost. Then BOAC offered to operate three Mk.IIs but only if they were guaranteed their losses by the government. The idea did not get far.

Test flying of the Mk.I continued. The Farnborough Show was visited again in September 1950, with further visits throughout 1951, including the Paris Airshow in July and another visit to Heathrow (minus tail mass balances) later the same month. Later trips included a round flight to the Orkneys and a visit to Prestwick, the Scottish national airport.

All this time the Brabazon Mk.II was being assembled in the centre bay of the assembly hall and was basically similar to the Mk.I, the big difference being the

The Douglas DC4 Skymaster, the military version of which was available in large numbers at the end of the war for cheap sale to the airlines. (courtesy: Janes).

The Lockheed Constellation, probably the best piston-engined airliner and which did much to demonstrate the unsuitability of the Brabazon. Some of these machines were based at Filton in the west bay of the Assembly Hall during the Brabazon project. (courtesy: KLM).

One of BOAC's Boeing Stratocruisers which was based at Filton and was a major competitor of the Brabazon. (courtesy: BA).

The partially assembled Brabazon Mk II. in the centre bay of the Assembly Hall with the pressure test specimen alongside. In the bottom left is a Boeing B29 Washington bomber, 88 of which were modified at Filton for service in the RAF in 1951–52.

Demolition of the Brabazon Mk. I proceeding in the west bay on 2nd October, 1953. The Mk. II awaits her turn in a corner of the hangar. The remnant carrying the name awaits transfer to a museum – today it is in the Bristol Industrial Museum.

proposed use of the Proteus gas turbine and the greatly enhanced performance that was expected: a speed of 330mph at 35,000 ft. Installation of the Proteus meant that basic modifications to the inner wing were required, including jet pipe mountings. The undercarriage was also revised to take 4-wheel bogies on each main leg, an arrangement which worked well in the later Britannia.

A change made in the skinning of the Mk.II had an unexpected result. The Mk.I had been skinned in natural aluminium-clad sheets, which looked attractive, but in the Mk.II, the sheets were anodised light grey, control of the process being critical to maintain standard colour. One dark grey plate was riveted in before anyone realised what had happened and stood out like a sore thumb. The dark panel was still there when the airframe was broken up.

Construction of the Mk.II proceeded to the stage of fitting the dummy undercarriage, so that the shell could be taken out of the hangar and placed on the apron where both aircraft were photographed together. Then, in March 1952, Duncan Sandys, Minister of Supply, announced that work on the Brabazon Mk.II and two of the Princess boats was being suspended.

Test flying of the Brabazon Mk.I continued through the summer of 1952 but the fatigue problems, with cracks in the engine support structures, continued to give trouble. Anti-vibration fittings failed to solve the problem and then more fatigue problems were discovered in the inner wing box structure. From these indications, it was possible to calculate an airframe life of only 5,000 hours, a totally unacceptable figure for airworthiness certification. In addition, Bill Pegg had flight tested the new Britannia on 16th August, 1952 and the company wished to concentrate its skilled resources on the development of the new machine. The end was coming.

The Bristol Type 167 Brabazon Mk.I made her last flight on 20th September, 1952, by which date she had made 164 flights for a total of 382 hours 15 minutes flight time. The flight test programme was largely complete and the company pronounced itself satisfied with the results. Both aircraft were stored in the Assembly Hall awaiting disposal instructions.

The company had to wait until a House of Commons statement by Duncan Sandys, on 17th July, 1953, confirmed that the Brabazon project was to end and that both aircraft would be scrapped. The aborted project was lampooned by some commentators as a costly white elephant, while Bristol's *Evening Post* caught the local mood with its headline: 'And so Farewell to the Great Might-Have-Been'.

All the equipment that could be salvaged was removed and then on a Monday morning in October, the scrap team from Coley of Hounslow arrived at Filton.

The firm were specialists in the recovery of scrap metal from unwanted aircraft, and the saying 'Coley's got it' was a popular euphemism throughout the industry in those days. It took the Coley team two weeks to demolish the work of twenty years, and when they had finished, there remained just one piece of fuselage carrying the aircraft name (today in Bristol Industrial Museum) and the nose oleo leg (in London's Science Museum), while the gust alleviator vane was recovered by a well known test pilot.

The Brabazon had passed into history.

SEVEN

Epilogue

'The air is an uninterrupted, navigable ocean which comes to the threshold of every man's door.'

Sir George Cayley, British aviation pioneer, 1852

That first flight of the Brabazon I on Sunday, 4th September, 1949, was not quite 46 years after the first flight of the Wright Brothers at Kill Devil Hill, Kitty Hawk on 17th December 1903. Both events had at least one thing in common. Before either could occur, a great deal of patient trial and research had to take place. Aviation has been nothing if not the dominant science of the twentieth century and there are many who would argue that the advance from the Wright Flyer to the Brabazon was greater than anything that has happened in the half century that has passed since. This is not to forget that the moon landing and the first flights of Concorde and the Boeing 747 all took place in the epic year of 1969, just twenty years on from the first flight of the Brabazon. This gives some idea of the break-neck pace at which aviation has developed.

So what did the Brabazon do for the science of aviation? Many of those who were present on that September morning in 1949 have inevitably passed from the scene – Lord Brabazon, Sir Stanley White, Sir Reginald Verdon Smith, Stanley Hooker, Frank Owner, Sir Archibald Russell, Fred Pollicutt and Bill Pegg and most of his crew. What was their vision of the future on that day? Did they achieve their aim? These were all pragmatic men and they did nothing without purpose and careful thought.

The first aim was simple and certainly achieved. It was to build the largest civil landplane in the world and fly it in safety and comfort in all weathers. This they did and only three aeroplanes of comparable size were around at the same time.

Two of them, both flying boats – the Princess and the Hercules – were failures but the third, the Convair B36, went into series production as a long-range nuclear bomber for the USAF. These aircraft pointed the way with stress skin construction and today the line production of very large aircraft is commonplace.

Few modern aircraft have exceeded the Brabazon in size and weight, apart from US and Russian freighters. The wingspan of 230ft compares with the 193ft of the Boeing 747, which has been the largest civil airliner in production for almost thirty years, with no sign of orders falling off.

There were other legacies from the Brabazon. In a TV programme, Sir Archibald Russell said that the Brabazon introduced 'new flying controls, new engines, new hydraulics, new electrics, new undercarriage controls and new instrumentation, and when you've got all that, there isn't much old that's left!'

In this, Russell was right, for the design studies that were done for Brab controls in particular were carried on with refined power units and servo tabs in the Britannia airliner. Further developments eventually appeared in Concorde. The high power electrical systems which first went into the Brab are now used worldwide. The list continues.

The whole Brabazon project cost the British Treasury £12 million at a time when the pound sterling was worth £18 at today's values. £5½ million of this went into the development and construction of the two aircraft, while the runway and Assembly Hall cost the remaining £6½ million. In retrospect, this installation has been the Brabazon's most valuable 'spin off', for it turned Filton into the leading aircraft production centre in the UK, and one of the top two or three in Europe.

The runway remains one of the longest in the world and is capable of taking any existing aircraft. Envious eyes are occasionally cast on it as the potential centre of a new civic airport for the South West, and the argument over that possibility is not yet over.

Adjacent to the runway, the great Assembly Hall dominates the north Bristol skyline and is a landmark for miles around, as it has been since 1948. As soon as the Brabazon II was scrapped, the assembly jigs for the Britannia were laid down and the Assembly Hall has been used as Filton's production centre ever since. Here the Britannia was produced in series of versions until it was replaced in the sixties and seventies by the brilliant Anglo-French Concorde, and all British Concordes were built and flown from there.

The Assembly Hall is a versatile facility and many types of aircraft have been serviced or converted there. At the very beginning in 1950 came the Constellations

The giant Saunders Roe Princess flying boat (219ft span, 10 Bristol Proteus turbo-props) rivalled the Brabazon in size but was cancelled even while the prototype was making its spectacular first flights. The same engines should have powered the Brabazon Mk II. (courtesy: Saro).

The huge wooden Hughes H4 Hercules, the largest aircraft ever to fly, which it did for about one mile at a height of 50ft on 2nd November, 1947. With eight 3,000hp Pratt & Whitney radial engines, it spanned 320ft (90ft longer than the Brab) and could accommodate up to 700 passengers. It never flew again. (courtesy: Lockheed).

and Stratocruisers of BOAC and, long forgotten, B29 Washingtons for the RAF, followed by a batch of Type 170 Freighters intended for the Pakistan Air Force. Vickers Valiants were converted for radar avoidance low flying and the Bristol Type 221 (the last Bristol type number) were assembled there. Later on, Lightning V noses were assembled and old Vickers VC10 airliners turned into air-to-air refuelling tankers for the Royal Air Force. As the last decade of the century began, the Hall was turning out centre fuselages for the BAe 146 Feederliner and new accommodation was being added for the assembly of wings for the Airbus A320.

By any standard, the Hall has a formidable record of service to the aviation industry: all in direct line from the Brabazon. With the runway, it is the Brabazon project's enduring legacy.

The Bristol Aeroplane Company was long ago absorbed into British Aerospace and that company has invested in Filton in a major way for its Airbus programme where it designs and manufactures wing components. So perhaps it is one of the happier accidents of history that BAe Airbus at Filton is scheming plans for the giant Airbus A3XX, a giant twin-decked 600-plus seater airliner for the world's air routes. How Reggie Verdon Smith and Archibald Russell and their band of brothers at Filton would have enjoyed working on that – and solving today's problems as they met and solved those of yesterday.

The Brabazon legacy: the Bristol Britannia assembly line in full swing in the Assembly Hall in the mid-fifties.

The Brabazon legacy: Concordes being assembled in the centre bay in the 1970s.

The Brabazon legacy: Concorde G-BOAC inaugurates the first transatlantic supersonic service to Washington DC on 24th May, 1976.

A model of the proposed Airbus A3XX, a worthy successor to the Brabazon project.

Technical Specification

BRABAZON
(Bristol 167 Mark I)

MAIN DIMENSIONS

Span	230 ft 0 in
Length	177 ft 0 in
Height	50 ft 0 in
Undercarriage wheelbase	64 ft 0 in
Undercarriage track	55 ft 0 in

FUSELAGE CAPACITY ..... 25,000 cu ft

WING

Wing area (gross)	5,317 sq ft
Aspect ratio	10
Maximum depth	6 ft 6 in
Aerofoil section (laminar flow)	Root T.P.4 (mod.) Tip T.P.5
Root chord (centre-line of fuselage, leading edge and trailing edge produced)	31 ft 0 in
Tip chord	10 ft
Thickness/chord ratio (root)	0.21
Thickness/chord ratio (tip)	0.15
Dihedral (outer plane)	2 deg.
Incidence	+3 deg. 30 min.
Sweepback of leading edge (inner wing)	4 deg. 16 min.
Sweepback of leading edge (outer wing)	14 deg. 56 min.
Taper ratio $\left\{ \dfrac{\text{tip chord}}{\text{root chord}} \right\}$	0.32

TAILPLANE

Span	75 ft 0 in
Tailplane and elevator area (gross)	1,103 sq ft
Tailplane and elevator aspect ratio	5
Tailplane dihedral	0 deg.
Tailplane incidence	+2 deg.

FIN AND RUDDER

Total area (including dorsal fin)	692 sq ft
Aspect ratio	1.3
Rudder range	25 deg. port 25 deg. starboard

ELEVATOR

Total area	264 sq ft
Range up	25 deg. 0 min.
Range down	15 deg. 0 min.

AILERONS

Span (each)	43 ft
Area (each)	185 sq ft
Range up	20 deg. 0 min.
Range down	20 deg. 0 min.

FLAPS

Total area	682 sq ft
Settings: Full	50 deg. 0 min.
Take-off	20 deg. 0 min.
Approach	50 deg. 0 min.

WEIGHTS

Gross weight .... 290,000 lb
Operational weight (weight
    less fuel and payload) ...... 169,500 lb
Maximum landing weight .... 240,000 lb
Weight for first flight .... 200,000 lb

LOADINGS

Wing loading .... 50.4 lb/sq ft
Power loading .... 14.5 lb/sq ft

ACCOMMODATION

Crew of 6–12 and 100 passengers (maximum)

ENGINES

Number — 8

Type — Bristol Centaurus 20 eighteen-cylinder, sleeve-valve, air-cooled, arrangement in pairs in inner wing, driving independent co-axial counter-rotating airscrews

Capacity — 3,270 cu in (53.6 litres)

Take-off output — 2,500 h.p.

Maximum continuous power ("M" blower) — 2,190 h.p. at 5,000 ft

Maximum weak-mixture cruising power ("S" blower) — 1,640 h.p. at 22,000 ft

Maximum climbing power — 2,190 h.p. at 5,000 ft

AIRSCREWS

8 Rotol constant speed, fully feathered and reversing

Number of blades ...... 3 per airscrew
Operation .... Hydro-electric
Diameter .... 16 ft 0 in
Pitch range (fine) .... Front, 16 deg.
                          Rear, 14 deg. 30 min.
Pitch setting (feathered) . Front, 84 deg. 30 min.
.... Rear, 84 deg. 30 min.
Reverse .... Front, minus 18 deg. 5 min.
.... Rear, minus 16 deg. 40 min.

FUEL AND OIL CAPACITIES

Fuel (each wing) .... 6,750 usable, 78 unusable
Fuel capacity (total) .... 13,650 gal
Number of fuel tanks ... 28
Oil capacity (total) ..... 450 gal

PERFORMANCE (ESTIMATED)

Cruising speed .... 250 m.p.h. at 25,000 ft
Maximum speed .... 300 m.p.h. at 25,000 ft
Rate of climb at sea level 750 ft/min
Service ceiling .... 25,000 ft (increasing as fuel is consumed)
Range .... 5,460 miles at 250 m.p.h. at 25,000 ft

121

Bibliography and Sources

Barnes, C.H. *Bristol Aircraft Since 1910*, Putnam 3rd 1988
Green, G. *Bristol Aerospace since 1910*, Private 1985
Gunston, Bill *By Jupiter – the life of Sir Roy Fedden*, Royal Ae. Society 1978
Hooker, Sir Stanley *Not Much of an Engineer*, Airlife 1984
King, Peter *Knights of the Air*, Constable 1989
Penrose, Harald *Ominous Skies 1935–1939*, HMSO 1980
Pegg, Bill *Sent Flying*, Macdonald 1959
Pudney, John *Bristol Fashion*, Private 1960
Russell, Sir Archibald *A Span of Wings*, Airlife 1992
Wakefield, Kenneth *Target Filton*, Redcliffe 2nd 1990
Wall, Robert *Airliners*, Collins 1980

Further sources include the files of:

Newspapers – *The Times, The Financial Times, Bristol Evening Post, Bristol Evening World*
Periodicals – *Flight, The Aeroplane, RAeS Journal & papers, The Bristol Review*

The Bristol Aero Collection has accumulated an archive of material on Bristol aircraft and the author has drawn freely on the Brabazon section of that archive.

Acknowledgements

The author is very grateful to Howard Berry, Director of Public Affairs, and David Charlton, Head of Photographic Services, British Aerospace Airbus plc for the supply of and permission to use photographs from the British Aerospace archives. Oliver and Mary Dearden of the Bristol Aero Collection encouraged the author to write this book and he is grateful to them for the help they gave with archive material from the collection, and to his fellow trustees for permission to use the archives. The author will always be grateful for the help he received in earlier years on this and other projects from the late Sir Reginald Verdon Smith and the late Sir Archibald Russell, both of whom were full of wise counsel. Derek Frise provided recollections of his uncle. Others who helped include Walter Gibb, DSO., DFC., Sir George White, Bart., and the many ex-colleagues of the author who worked at the Filton factory and recalled so much of the Brabazon story. Among these are Fred Burnell, Fred Price, Alf Samuels, Roger Presswood, the late Ron Jenkins and Roy Jones. The Clifton Pro-Lab, Bristol restored archive photographs.

The writing of this book brought back many recollections of the late Frank Chard, project manager of the Brabazon, who taught the author about aircraft and management and whose memory he treasures to this day.

Except where indicated in the captions, all illustrations in this book have been supplied by courtesy of British Aerospace plc, Civil Aerospace Division.

Finally, the author thanks his publisher, John Sansom of Redcliffe Press Ltd, who had the original idea of a book on the Brab. He also thanks his wife Jean for her support during the writing of another book!

Index

Entries in **bold** refer to illustrations and captions. General references to Bristol, Filton, Patchway, the two world wars etc appear frequently in the text and are not listed in this index.